heal

healthy eating &
abundant living

your diet-free, faith-based guide to a fabulous life

Group

Incredible things will happen

Loveland, Colorado

www.group.com

Allie Marie Smith and Judy Halliday

Group resources actually work!

This Group resource incorporates our R.E.A.L. approach to ministry. It reinforces a growing friendship with Jesus, encourages long-term learning, and results in life transformation, because it's

Relational
Learner-to-learner interaction enhances learning and builds Christian friendships.

Experiential
What learners experience through discussion and action sticks with them up to 9 times longer than what they simply hear or read.

Applicable
The aim of Christian education is to equip learners to be both hearers and doers of God's Word.

Learner-based
Learners understand and retain more when the learning process takes into consideration how they learn best.

HEAL: Healthy Eating and Abundant Living
Your Diet-Free, Faith-Filled Guide to a Fabulous Life
Copyright © 2008 Allie Smith and Judy Halliday

Visit our website: **group.com/women**

Credits
Authors: Allie Marie Smith and Judy Halliday
Copy Editor: Ann Jahns
Executive Developer: Amy Nappa
Print Production Artist: Perfect Type and Shelly Dillon
Chief Creative Officer: Joani Schultz
Production Manager: DeAnne Lear
Art Director/Cover Art Director/Designer: Andrea Filer

Unless otherwise noted, Scripture taken from the *HOLY BIBLE*, NEW INTERNATIONAL VERSION®. Copyright © 1973, 1978, 1984 by International Bible Society. Used by permission of Zondervan Publishing House. All rights reserved.

Library of Congress Cataloging-in-Publication Data

Smith, Allie Marie, 1983-
  HEAL, healthy eating and abundant living : your diet-free, faith-filled guide to a fabulous life / Allie Smith and Judy Halliday.
    p. cm.
  ISBN 978-0-7644-3735-9 (pbk. : alk. paper)
  1. Nutrition—Religious aspects—Christianity. 2. Health—Religious aspects—Christianity. 3. Christian life. I. Halliday, Judy. II. Title.

  RA784.S57 2008
  613.2--dc22

                                  2008027527
10 9 8 7 6 5 4 3 2 1   17 16 15 14 13 12 11 10 09 08
Printed in the United States of America.

Please note that it is important to consult your physician anytime you begin a new health or exercise program. This resource and the information contained within this resource are not intended to replace a one-on-one consultation with a medical physician. Medical issues and certain medications can often interfere with your weight and overall health, so we encourage you to seek professional medical advice.

Table of Contents

Acknowledgements

Allie Marie Smith

I am humbled with gratitude to my Savior and Redeemer—the One who met me in my brokenness and breathed life into the empty parts of my soul. Jesus, you have healed me and set me free. I am grateful for a life spent with you and am privileged to be called your daughter.

To my coastal cowboy, best friend, biggest fan, and life companion—thank you for keeping a smile on my face and filling my days with laughter, joy, affection, and adventure. I love you!

To Mom and Dad—no amount of words will ever be able to express the gratitude and love I have for you. You have been my pillar of strength. Thank you for carrying me through the storms I've encountered with grace, unconditional love, and determination; and thank you for opportunities you've generously afforded me. I love you more than you know.

To Judy—you are a woman of exquisite, unfading beauty whose authentic faith draws me closer to God. This would only be a dream without you. Thanks for believing in the dreams God has put within me and for sharing your time, wisdom, love, and life with me. And thank you for leading the way to freedom for this generation of women through the message and ministry of *Thin Within*. God has blessed me more than I could have ever imagined by bringing you into my life.

I am especially grateful to the girls in Wonderfully Made and to those whose time, passion, openness, leadership, and input have been instrumental in this work: Kayla Mertes, Meghan Incorvaia, Janelle Bosko, and everyone who has been a part of the *HEAL* Journey. A special thank you to those who've shared your story of *HEALing* for this book and a big hug of thanks to Brittany Strayer for being the first to believe in this message and inspire other girls to embark on this journey!

To Christina DiMari, for sharing this work with the team at Group without me even knowing! And to my editor Amy Nappa—you are a joy to work with. Thank you for recognizing the need for this message.

To each one of my kindred spirits, my closest friends—thank you for sharing your dreams, laughter, struggles, and triumphs with me. I am blessed to do life with you!

And a huge hug of thanks to each of these amazing women who have been a blessing in my life: Grandma & Nana, Helen Ramos, Shirley & Alana Beyer, Christina DiMari, Debbie Ulrick, Kenon Neal, Jen McCarthy, Marcia Wallis, Momma Smith, Kimberlee Sherman, Nicole Bromley, Naomi McCotter, Mary Miller, and Virginia Luthman.

Judy Halliday

I praise God that in his sovereignty he orchestrated the divine meeting with my beloved sister Allie, a young woman who is wise beyond her years with a beauty that reflects the calling and passion God has placed on her life. I eagerly await all that our Redeemer and Lord intends for the young women of today as he uses his faithful servant to carry forth his message of healing and hope to generations to come.

I rejoice in the privilege it's been for me to meet many special Wonderfully Made girls, among them Kayla Mertes, who genuinely reflects the love of Jesus.

Judy & Allie

Introduction

Welcome to the *Healthy Eating and Abundant Living* journey, a movement of women like you who are courageously rising above the strongholds of food, eating, and body image and choosing to walk upon the unbeaten path toward living a fulfilling life of health, love, joy, friendship, and service.

When it comes to the areas of food, eating, and body image, many women are desperate for healing. We're a generation of women obsessed with what we're going to put into our mouths and the number that's going to show up on the scale. We have a love-hate relationship with food, fashion, and our reflection. Because our bodies don't feel "good enough," we don't feel good enough. We try to control the craziness in our lives by controlling our eating, or we escape it all by stuffing ourselves sick. We're blessed with an abundance of food we don't know what to do with. We feel empty, lifeless, stuck, and desperate for more. But this isn't the life we've been created for! The woman God designed you to be can be healed and made whole in body, mind, and spirit. The truth is that we are loved.

Because of this love we have hope. We have a God who wants to *heal* us and restore us to be the women he created us to be. As you open your heart to be healed by his love, you'll find yourself joyfully living in more light than you ever dreamed possible. You will have the joy of seeing your body, mind, and spirit transformed from within, as God tenderly molds you into the beautiful woman he's created you to be. May you embark on this journey with a newfound hope for healing, with God as your confidence, healer, and friend.

Love,

♡Allie

Allie and Judy

Endorsements

Allie Marie Smith has put together a wonderful plan for a healthy life. Having raised three daughters and listened to the pain of hundreds of others, I can't think of a more practical resource than *HEAL: Healthy Eating and Abundant Living*. This is more than a book with great insight, it's a God-honoring experience to read, reflect, and react to establish a proper foundation for living life to the fullest. This material is written by someone who definitely knows and understands the issues of young women in this generation.

Jim Burns, Ph.D.
President, HomeWord

Author of *Teaching Your Children Healthy Sexuality; The Purity Code; and 10 Building Blocks to a Solid Family*

Our world offers band-aids to the yearnings we feel deep within, yearnings that only true understanding of God's love and acceptance can quench. In her first book, HEAL, Allie will help you identify your hurts and hungers so you can bring them fully to Christ, where every craving finds complete fulfillment. Allie has walked this path and will guide you in the right direction!

Andrea Stephens

Author of *Glamour Girls* and founder of the B.A.B.E. Event for teen girls

What a delightful partnership between Allie and Judy—youthful commitment combined with proven wisdom! In this book you will find an abundance of both. This book sees women as whole people and offers realistic help to them in practical ways. No crazy diets to follow, no super-spiritualized advice given. Just straightforward and hopeful talk about the issues that plague so many in our culture today. In helping women explore the underlying issues that drive them to food without undue navel-gazing, this work approaches the issues of disordered eating, body image, and cultural pressure in such a way that individuals and small groups who use it will find a path to help and healing. I will certainly be recommending this book in the future.

Travis Stewart, LPC, MATS
Ministry Relations, Remuda Ranch

Co-Founder of the True Campaign

If you want to experience true freedom, balance, and the abundant life God has dreamed for you, then you will love this study! Packed with wisdom, insight, and encouragement, HEAL will guide you in becoming the shining star God designed you to be!

Christina DiMari

Author of *You're Designed to Shine* and *Ocean Star*

HEAL is a much needed book for so many women I have crossed paths with—women who are literally starving for love, hope, and true identity. The freedom and encouragement found within these pages provide all of us with a breath of fresh air and a newfound joy for the journey of healing ahead. Practical, fun, full of wisdom, personal stories, and hope for healing, HEAL is a must-read for all women!

Nicole Bromley

Speaker and author of *Hush: Moving from Silence to Healing after Childhood Sexual Abuse*

In a market glutted with books that capitalize on the epidemic of eating and body image issues among women, it is refreshing to come upon material that clearly puts the reader first. The fresh voice of Allie Marie Smith, combined with the seasoned perspective of Judy Halliday—a pioneer in Christ-centered approaches to eating issues—makes for a comprehensive yet practical tool for all who seek freedom from the tyranny of the scale.

Constance Rhodes
Founder and CEO, FINDINGbalance

Author of *Life Inside the "Thin" Cage: A Personal Look into the Hidden World of the Chronic Dieter*

Whether [you are] a binge eater, restrictive eater, or somewhere in between, HEAL provides the insight and tools to help establish a healthy relationship with food. Written clearly and concisely, it will inspire women of all ages to appreciate, respect, and care for their uniquely designed, God-given bodies.

Ann Capper, RD, CDN
Nutrition Editor, FINDINGbalance.com

Author of *Big Thighs, Tight Jeans: Should Jan Go on a Diet?*

How to Use This Book

This "guide to a fabulous life" is designed to be done with a small group of four to 10 girls or women. (And let us just say right now, we refer to women of all ages as "girls," so no matter how young or old you are—we're talking to you!) You can also go through this guide without a small group if you prefer.

If you have a group larger than this, we encourage you to break into smaller groups during your weekly meetings. There are six lessons total, which include both a personal study section (that you do yourself) and a group study outline (that you do with others). It's up to your group to decide if you'd like to do the study in six weeks or span it out across 12 weeks—whatever works best for your group's schedule and needs!

We encourage you to work through each lesson at your own pace. We've found it works great to spread the personal lesson out over the week, giving you plenty of time to absorb the material and not feel rushed or overwhelmed.

When you gather with others for the group portion, we recommend having one or two facilitators depending on the size of your group. You can always break into smaller groups of four or five, each one with a facilitator, to make the sharing time more personal and allow everyone a chance to talk. Each girl needs her own copy of this book so she can journal in it and make it her own!

Accountability and friendships are a core part of the *HEAL* Journey, and our hope is that you embrace this wholeheartedly. Our desire is that this will be a place where you feel welcomed, safe, and valued. We ask you to treat your sisters as you'd like to be treated, holding all information private, with respect, and in total confidentiality. We're so excited for you to join us on this life-changing venture and pray that God will shine his face upon this freedom-filled journey.

Accountability Moments

Throughout each individual lesson you'll come across a box that says "Accountability Moment." Every time you reach this road mark, we encourage you to give one of your sisters on the *HEAL* Journey a call. Keep it short—maybe around five to 10 minutes. If you'd like to talk longer, consider meeting up for a walk or a cup of coffee. This is a chance for you to focus on encouraging someone else, which includes listening to her and praying for her. This is also a chance to bring to light anything you are struggling with yourself and ask for support and prayer. It's up to your group to decide if you're going to have the same accountability partners each week or mix it up week by week.

Free Space

Each session includes a blank page. This is your creative or free space to enjoy as you like! Make a collage, journal, write down verses, or draw a picture. It's up to you!

The *HEAL* Principles

• *HEAL* is a shared journey.

"Two are better than one, because they have a good return for their work: If one falls down, his friend can help him up. But pity the man who falls and has no one to help him up!" Ecclesiastes 4:9-10

Our struggles with food and our body tend to be at their worst when we're isolated or surrounded by a negative community. Authentic healing requires you to consciously step out of the darkness and into the light. Much of this light awaits you in a community of like-minded women who are also walking toward freedom in this area of their lives. You're not alone. You have a God who loves you and wants to see you through this and bring his children to encourage you as you begin to cultivate a positive approach to food, your body, and life.

• *HEAL* is centered on God, not ourselves or worldly wisdom.

"So whether you eat or drink or whatever you do, do it all for the glory of God." 1 Corinthians 10:31

HEAL is a Christ-centered program—one that is grounded in God. Built upon biblical wisdom, *HEAL* encourages you to bring God into your daily interactions with food while also allowing him to heal the deepest hungers of your heart. You'll learn how to take your eyes and hearts off of food and fix them upon the Lord. Experience has taught us that we need something bigger than ourselves to heal and restore us—because we can't do it on our own. Girls are encouraged to surrender their food and body struggles to God, believing that it is his desire to restore and heal them as his daughters.

• *HEAL* offers a freedom-filled approach to food.

"It is for freedom that Christ has set us free. Stand firm, then, and do not let yourselves be burdened again by a yoke of slavery." Galatians 5:1

On your *HEAL* Journey you'll be challenged to give up restrictive eating, calorie counting, weighing and measuring, and other diet-like practices as you learn how to approach food with freedom and confidence. Dieting only intensifies your focus on food, your body, and yourself. *HEAL* teaches that the key to both reaching and maintaining your God-mandated (not media-mandated) size is to become aware of and obey your stomach's hunger and fullness cues. This sets us on the path toward reaching our natural, healthy, and God-given size.

• *HEAL* is a lifestyle.

"Being confident of this, that he who began a good work in you will carry it on to completion until the day of Christ Jesus." Philippians 1:6

HEAL is not a diet. It is a lifestyle of inward transformation and lasting change that you can carry with you for the rest of your life. We are continually changed from within as we surrender our lives to Jesus and allow him to continue the good work he has begun in each of us.

• *HEAL* is about living an abundant life.

"I have come that they may have life, and have it to the full. I give them eternal life, and they shall never perish; no one can snatch them out of my hand." John 10:10, 28

HEAL is dedicated to inspiring you to live a more meaningful and abundant life.

Many diet programs lead you on to think that once you have your ideal body, you will have the perfect life. This is a lie! We've been created for so much more, and *HEAL* inspires you on this journey toward truth and transformation. It's time to step away from the words of the world and embrace the words of the Father. We have to get our eyes, hearts, and thoughts off of food and on to a deeper relationship with God. You need to trust and know that the plans God has in store for you are plans to prosper you and not to harm you—to give you a hope and a future. He has created you with unique beauty, gifts, talents, and experiences. He longs to see you used to love and serve the world around you. This is the abundant life he has for you.

Now, let's get started, girl! We're so glad you're here!

Psalm 139

1 O Lord, you have searched me
    and you know me.

2 You know when I sit and when I rise;
    you perceive my thoughts from afar.

3 You discern my going out and my lying down;
    you are familiar with all my ways.

4 Before a word is on my tongue
    you know it completely, O Lord.

5 You hem me in—behind and before;
    you have laid your hand upon me.

6 Such knowledge is too wonderful for me,
    too lofty for me to attain.

7 Where can I go from your Spirit?
    Where can I flee from your presence?

8 If I go up to the heavens, you are there;
    if I make my bed in the depths, you are there.

9 If I rise on the wings of the dawn,
    if I settle on the far side of the sea,

10 even there your hand will guide me,
    your right hand will hold me fast.

11 If I say, "Surely the darkness will hide me
    and the light become night around me,"

12 even the darkness will not be dark to you;
    the night will shine like the day,
    for darkness is as light to you.

13 For you created my inmost being;
    you knit me together in my mother's womb.

14 I praise you because I am fearfully and
    wonderfully made;
    your works are wonderful,
    I know that full well.

15 My frame was not hidden from you
    when I was made in the secret place.
    When I was woven together in the depths of
        the earth,

16 your eyes saw my unformed body.
    All the days ordained for me
    were written in your book
    before one of them came to be.

17 How precious to me are your thoughts, O God!
    How vast is the sum of them!

18 Were I to count them,
    they would outnumber the grains of sand.
    When I awake,
    I am still with you.

19 If only you would slay the wicked, O God!
    Away from me, you bloodthirsty men!

20 They speak of you with evil intent;
    your adversaries misuse your name.

21 Do I not hate those who hate you, O Lord,
    and abhor those who rise up against you?

22 I have nothing but hatred for them;
    I count them my enemies.

23 Search me, O God, and know my heart;
    test me and know my anxious thoughts.

24 See if there is any offensive way in me,
    and lead me in the way everlasting.

Lesson 1: You Are Wonderfully Made

Personal Study

Remember, you don't have to do the entire personal study section in one day. Take your time. Reflect. Journal. Let the words really sink in!

You Are Wonderfully Made

If there's one truth every girl longs to know, it's that she is wonderfully made. I still remember the time I came across the verse in Psalm 139 containing this truth. It was like I'd finally found what I was looking for, like something I'd been longing to hear my entire life was spoken to me and I could finally rest easy, secure in the truth behind those two words.

We are hungry to know that we are wonderfully made—to know that we're esteemed, of high value, beloved, and set apart. When we *don't* know and experience the freedom offered in this truth, we turn to things that promise to fill this void—food, false intimacy with guys, perfectionism, a hot body, an eagerness to please. We give ourselves away because we don't know who we are or to whom we belong.

You Have a Maker

Being wonderfully made means that you have a Maker—a Maker who made you and made you beautifully; a Maker who loves you and knows you, has amazing plans for you, and longs to reveal to you your value and worth as his daughter. Walking in the truth that you're wonderfully made is not only the key to experiencing authentic healing in your relationship with food and your body, but it opens the way to an awesome and abundant life.

my reflections

God never intended for us to struggle with food and body confidence as we do. He made our bodies perfect in his image. Genesis 1:27 says, "So God created man in his own image, in the image of God he created him; male and female he created them."

As little girls, many of us were blind to what the world had to say about our bodies. We didn't know that one day we would be pressured to look a certain way. Our bodies were simply a way to explore the wonders of the world—bodies were for twirling and skipping and laughing out loud. But as we ventured from the innocence of our youth, the world began to tell us otherwise. It told us that the shape of our bodies reflects the level of our worth. That place of girlhood freedom we've left behind is where God still intends for us to live, and to live abundantly—to live in freedom and confidence, content in the way our bodies have been made.

- What would it be like to live in a state of "girlhood freedom"—to live with joy and confidence, content and at peace with your body? Describe your thoughts and feelings about this kind of mindset.

- Reflect on the people, events, or circumstances that may have influenced how you currently view your body and relate to food.

- What does it mean to you to know that you are fearfully and wonderfully made?

Fashioned by the Hands of God

Of all God's creations, we are his masterpiece. Psalm 139:13-14 says, "For you created my inmost being; you knit me together in my mother's womb. I praise you because I am fearfully and wonderfully made; your works are wonderful, I know that full well."

As I was babysitting my friend's 7-week-old little girl one night, I marveled at the incredible way God created her. It was amazing to think that at one time I'd been a little baby just like her. We are God's little miracles...his children—wholly and dearly loved.

Ephesians 2:10 says we are "God's workmanship." Knowing that we are fearfully and wonderfully made by his hands, we can trust that God knew what he was doing when he gave us the natural signals of hunger and fullness. These signals will be your internal compass on your *HEAL* Journey that can guide you toward or help you maintain the size you were designed to be.

- Psalm 139:15 says, "When I was woven together in the depths of the earth, your eyes saw my unformed body." Meditate for a few minutes on what this verse is saying. What do you think it means that God's eyes saw your unformed body?

A Breath of Fresh Air

On the *HEAL* Journey you are challenged to do away with "worldly" ways of thinking about food and your body. These are the messages we see and hear around us each day through the media, through conversations with others, and through our overall environment. As you embark on this new journey and begin to rely on God for guidance as you eat and live, you'll be liberated from diet rules, emotional eating, compulsive exercise, and other prisons that may have consumed you. This is a freedom-filled approach to food.

To experience authentic healing and restoration, we need to focus on something bigger than ourselves. *Healthy Eating and Abundant Living* is about bringing God into the center of your life and giving him the struggles with your body, weight, and eating.

One girl on the *HEAL* Journey said, "Although I already had a relationship with God, I never thought about going to him with my struggles with my body and food. It was like it was my thing. But now after *HEAL,* I can't imagine going anywhere but to God with this area of my life. I realize now that he is the only One who can heal and restore me."

- Have you ever tried on your own to change or make peace with your body? If so, what was this experience like?

my reflections

my reflections

_____
_____
_____
_____
_____
_____
_____
_____
_____
_____
_____
_____
_____
_____
_____
_____
_____
_____
_____
_____
_____
_____

The Woman God Created You to Be

As you draw nearer to God in every area of your life, he'll reveal the truth about who you are as his child and guide you into becoming more of the amazing woman he has designed you to be—both spiritually and physically. As you begin to trust God with the way he made your body by obeying your God-given signals of hunger and satisfaction, you will have the joy of seeing your body transformed into its God-mandated (not media-mandated!) size.

- In what ways do you need to learn to trust God regarding the way he's made you?

- What are some practical ways you can begin to welcome God into every meal and eating experience?

Living in the Light

As daughters of God we are made to live in the light, but too often we opt for the darkness either because it's familiar and safe or because we're ashamed of our secrets.

When it comes to our interactions with food, many of us are experts at hiding things. We wait for everyone to go to bed to begin our midnight binge. We lock the bathroom door, turn on the fan, and run the faucets full blast while we make ourselves throw up. We tell our friends we just ate before we came. But the reality is, while we might be able to hide our secrets from the people in our lives, we can't hide from God.

In Psalm 139:11-12, David recognizes something about God we too easily forget. "If I say, 'Surely the darkness will hide me and the light become night around me,' even the darkness will not be dark to you; the night will shine like the day, for darkness is as light to you." Whatever your secrets might be, you can't fool God.

Jessica, a young woman on the *HEAL* Journey, shares her story of how she tried to hide:

Jessica's Story

"My eating disorder started off innocently. I began to work out a couple times a week and eat a healthier diet in order to look fit for my wedding. Then I lost weight and liked it. A secret obsession began to grow. I developed a fear of gaining weight, so I did everything in my power to prevent that.

"I had always suffered from stomach pain after eating, but I never went to the doctor so I just lived with the pain. I finally saw a doctor and was diagnosed with celiac disease, a food allergy to gluten, and was told I couldn't eat bread, pasta, cookies, pizza, processed foods, salad dressings, cakes, or many of the foods that were a regular part of my diet.

"I drastically lost weight, and secretly, I liked it. I began to intentionally starve myself and work out obsessively. I'd wake up at 6 a.m. and make it back before my husband woke up. I'd go again before or after lunch and once more after dinner. Everyone in my life began to notice my unhappiness and drastic weight loss but attributed it to my food allergy. It was a secret curtain I could hide behind. No one would ever know. But I knew and God knew."

It's in the light that our sin and shame is cleansed and wiped away. We must have bare-naked hearts that can be completely open and honest before God first, ourselves second, and others third.

Take some time with God to lay down the truth and bring to light anything you've been hiding or struggling with on your own. Reflect on the areas you've kept in the dark, and humbly ask God to meet you in those secret places. Write those thoughts here.

_____

_____

_____

_____

_____

my reflections

_____

_____

Prepare your heart before God. Quiet your spirit. Then pray:

Dear Jesus,

I come to you broken and tired from living in the dark. I realize that when I thought I was hiding in the darkness all alone, you were there right beside me. I know now that I am made to live and walk with you in the light. I give you my secrets. I give you my fears. Heal me, restore me, and wipe away my shame. Thank you for the gift of new life, and thank you for the light.

- Be completely honest with yourself. In what areas of your life are you living in the dark? Where do you need healing, but fear or shame has prevented this?

Open and Honest

We are going to challenge you to be open and honest with the girls accompanying you on this journey. You are made to live in sisterhood and community with one another and to live in the light with God.

Meghan, another sister on the *HEAL* Journey, shares her experience about stepping out of the darkness and into the light:

"During the time I struggled with anorexia, I was a part of a home group. This one night I was in total despair—weary and tired from trying to control everything. I knew I was going to cry and realized I could either cry alone and keep on hiding my struggle or I could go to home group and be with others in prayer. I fought the desire to keep my struggle hidden and decided to go.

"As I walked into the house, one of the leaders asked me how I was doing. The depth of my sorrow came forth and erupted in uncontrollable tears. Everything in me wanted to flee to my safe place of secrecy, where I could live alone, but in utter despair. I fought the temptation with all my strength, because deep down I knew God wanted me there. After worship my friend and another woman who had also struggled with an eating disorder prayed for me. As soon as I stepped into the light, I felt the bondage break. I saw that God had placed people in my life who wanted to walk with me out of the darkness, and I knew that as I stepped into the light, my journey toward healing had begun."

Meghan's Story

my reflections

• What struggles with food, your body, or just life are you sharing with those close to you?

Accountability Moment

Remember, now's the time to call a girlfriend and share with her how things are going—and hear how she's doing, too.

Made in Intimacy With God

We often don't recognize that there's a connection between what's drawing us to food, the pursuit of perfection (which doesn't exist!), or whatever we're filling ourselves with, and our inherent need for intimacy with God. We live in a world that threatens our relationship with

God. We are surrounded by counterfeits that claim to be the answer to what our hearts are seeking. But he is the only One who can truly satisfy our hungry hearts.

- In what areas of your life are you tempted to fulfill your need for intimacy apart from God?

- How can you begin to turn to God instead of these counterfeits?

My *HEAL* Journey

"Commit to the Lord whatever you do, and your plans will succeed." Proverbs 16:3

It's time to put the past behind you and move into the present—and take what you're learning on into the future. Before you meet with your group this week, take some time to journal about your relationship with food and your body at the following places on your journey.

Where I've been...

Where I am now...

Where I want to be...

_____

_____

_____

_____

Remember that God wants to tell you the truth about who you are. He wants to see the little girl in you come alive again, to be healed and made whole by his love and to rise up and fill the irreplaceable role on earth he has for you and only you. As you begin to bask in the truth that you are wonderfully made, you will begin to discover where your true value lies, and this truth will set you free.

Challenge

This week spend a significant amount of time acknowledging God's creation around you, shouting praises to God. Think about what it means to be "wonderfully made."

Memory Verse

"For you created my inmost being; you knit me together in my mother's womb. I praise you because I am fearfully and wonderfully made."
Psalm 139:13-14

Where I Am

Please take a few minutes to complete the following questionnaire. This will help you evaluate where you are, and as you move forward in your relationship with God, you'll be able to see how you're growing and changing. As you move along in the *HEAL* Journey, you may want to re-evaluate where you are. You can download additional copies of this at www.healjourney.com.

How would you rate the following areas of your life?

1. Health

0	1	2	3	4	5	6	7	8	9	10
Poor										Excellent

2. Energy level

0	1	2	3	4	5	6	7	8	9	10
Low										High

3. Friendships

0	1	2	3	4	5	6	7	8	9	10
Unsatisfying										Very Satisfying

4. School

0	1	2	3	4	5	6	7	8	9	10
Unsatisfying										Very Satisfying

5. Work

0	1	2	3	4	5	6	7	8	9	10
Unsatisfying										Very Satisfying

6. Relationship with God

0	1	2	3	4	5	6	7	8	9	10
Poor										Excellent

7. The degree to which you feel a part of a loving church community

| 0 | 1 | 2 | 3 | 4 | 5 | 6 | 7 | 8 | 9 | 10 |

Unsatisfying   Very Satisfying

8. Productivity

| 0 | 1 | 2 | 3 | 4 | 5 | 6 | 7 | 8 | 9 | 10 |

Low   High

9. Family relationships

| 0 | 1 | 2 | 3 | 4 | 5 | 6 | 7 | 8 | 9 | 10 |

Unsatisfying   Very Satisfying

10. How often are you aware of your body's hunger and fullness signals?

| 0 | 1 | 2 | 3 | 4 | 5 | 6 | 7 | 8 | 9 | 10 |

Always   Never

11. What hunger level are you usually at when you begin eating?

| -5 | -4 | -3 | -2 | -1 | 0 | 1 | 2 | 3 | 4 | 5 | 6 | 7 | 8 | 9 | 10 |

Undereating   Empty   Comfortable   Overeating

12. What hunger level are you usually at when you stop eating?

| -5 | -4 | -3 | -2 | -1 | 0 | 1 | 2 | 3 | 4 | 5 | 6 | 7 | 8 | 9 | 10 |

Undereating   Empty   Comfortable   Overeating

13. How often are you on a diet or restricting yourself of certain foods?

| 0 | 1 | 2 | 3 | 4 | 5 | 6 | 7 | 8 | 9 | 10 |

Never   Always

14. How often do you eat foods you really enjoy?

0   1   2   3   4   5   6   7   8   9   10

Never   Always

15. Your weight as a child (under 12 years old) was:

Underweight   Natural Weight   Somewhat Overweight   Very Overweight

16. While you were growing up, your mom's weight was:

Underweight   Natural Weight   Somewhat Overweight   Very Overweight

17. While you were growing up, your dad's weight was:

Underweight   Natural Weight   Somewhat Overweight   Very Overweight

18. You most often feel as though you are currently:

Underweight   Natural Weight   Somewhat Overweight   Very Overweight

19. How often do you feel confident about your body?

0   1   2   3   4   5   6   7   8   9   10

Never   Always

20. How often do you weigh yourself?

2+ times a day   Once a day   2-5 times a week   Rarely

21. How often do you speak negatively about your body (to yourself and others)?

0   1   2   3   4   5   6   7   8   9   10

Never   Always

22. How often do you think of yourself as a thin person?

0   1   2   3   4   5   6   7   8   9   10

Never   Always

23. What are some of the things you might be struggling with? Please rate the following items:

a. Depression

0   1   2   3   4   5   6   7   8   9   10

No Problem   Serious Problem

b. Alcohol abuse

0   1   2   3   4   5   6   7   8   9   10

No Problem   Serious Problem

c. Unhealthy relationships

0   1   2   3   4   5   6   7   8   9   10

No Problem   Serious Problem

d. Promiscuity

0   1   2   3   4   5   6   7   8   9   10

No Problem   Serious Problem

e. Drug use

0   1   2   3   4   5   6   7   8   9   10

No Problem   Serious Problem

f. Smoking

0   1   2   3   4   5   6   7   8   9   10

No Problem   Serious Problem

g. Starving myself

0   1   2   3   4   5   6   7   8   9   10

No Problem   Serious Problem

h. Disliking my body

0   1   2   3   4   5   6   7   8   9   10

No Problem   Serious Problem

i. Bingeing and purging

0   1   2   3   4   5   6   7   8   9   10

No Problem   Serious Problem

Free Space

Welcome to your personal creative space. Reflect on Lesson 1 by journaling, making a collage, or doing whatever you'd like to do!

Lesson 1: Group Study

You Are Wonderfully Made

Open your Bibles (or turn to page 13) and have one person in the group read Psalm 139 aloud as everyone follows along in their own Bibles.

Allow a few minutes for everyone to reflect on this psalm, and write down any thoughts or questions.

Then discuss this beautiful piece of Scripture verse by verse. Write down any insights from your discussion. Try to relate each verse to your relationship with food, eating, and your body.

_____

_____

_____

_____

_____

_____

_____

_____

_____

_____

_____

_____

_____

_____

_____

_____

_____

_____

Important Lessons From Psalm 139

- God is familiar with all our ways.

- We are fearfully and wonderfully made.

- We were made in absolute intimacy with our Maker. Our heart hungers to return to this place of intimacy, peace, and solitude before God.

- God's eyes saw our unformed body.

Activity—Living in the Light

Briefly take turns sharing your personal experiences regarding your weight, eating habits, and body image. Specifically discuss what you wrote in response to the three reflections from your personal study this week that begin on page 22 under "My *HEAL* Journey."

Sharing and Discussion

Use these questions to go deeper in your sharing. Be sure everyone has a chance to talk. (This might mean you need to form smaller groups or pairs.) And remember, what's shared here is shared in confidence.

- What does being "wonderfully made" mean to you?

- In what areas of your life have you been living in the dark?

- What scares you about living in the light?

- How have you hidden your struggles with food and your body from God and others?

- Reflect on the miracle of being knit together in your mother's womb.

Once you have finished sharing, form pairs and pray for each other. Pay special attention to the needs of your partner based upon what she shared.

Group Prayer

Close your time together with prayer.

A Mission to Give, a Mission to Heal

Fact: Americans spend over $40 billion a year on diet-related products.

Fact: Almost 30,000 children die every day, most due to hunger and treatable illnesses.

"From everyone who has been given much, much will be demanded; and from the one who has been entrusted with much, much more will be asked." —Jesus (Luke 12:48)

Girls, what can we do to help put things right?

As your group embarks on the *HEAL* Journey, we would like to invite you on a mission to give—a mission to heal. I would like your group to prayerfully consider sponsoring just one child (or more if you'd like!) through World Vision for only $30 a month. Just think, you'd only have to pitch in a few dollars depending on the size of your group—the cost of a vanilla latte! Girls, it's time to extend our hearts and our eyes outward—it's time to love and serve the world around us as Jesus calls us to.

To sponsor your child for only $30 a month through World Vision, visit www.world vision.org or call 1-888-511-6592. Then go to healjourney@gmail.com and let us know about your commitment.

---

my reflections

Lesson 2: The HEAL Basics

Personal Study

On this journey it's important for you to have a true understanding of what healthy eating really is. We're *not* talking about eating only a sugar-free, fat-free, purely organic, or low-carb diet. In fact, healthy eating has less to do with the *type* of food you eat and more to do with the *relationship* you have with food and God. Healthy eating in the *HEAL* sense is having an emotionally healthy approach to food. It means bringing God into the center of your relationship with food and learning to trust and obey the way he made you.

Not a Diet

I'm going to challenge you to do away with dieting. Diets and rigid "get-fit" plans don't address the root of the real problem in our lives. They overlook the underlying reasons why we may have an unhealthy relationship with food, our body, exercise, or other aspects of our lives. Diets give food the upper hand and attempt to fix our *appearance,* but not our *heart*.

I think God's take on dieting can be summed up in Colossians 2:20-23, which says, "Since you died with Christ to the basic principles of this world, why, as though you still belonged to it, do you submit to its rules: 'Do not handle! Do not taste! Do not touch!'? These are all destined to perish with use, because they are based on human commands and teachings. Such regulations indeed have an appearance of wisdom, with their self-imposed worship, their false humility and their harsh treatment of the body, but they lack any value in restraining sensual indulgence."

Through Christ we have died to the ways of the world! In relation to food, this means we can be done with the world's ways of dealing with food. We don't have to say goodbye to bread or chocolate or become a lifelong "weight-watcher." We can get off the scale (finally!) and get on with living an abundant life through Christ Jesus. Remember Galatians 5:1: "It is for freedom that Christ has set us free"! Don't bow down to the world's rules, but look up to the one who made you! *He* will set you free!

Dieting, obsessive exercise, disordered eating, and obsession with our physical appearance prevent us from being the women God has created us to be. Such bondage keeps you from being a woman whose gaze is fixed outward and who can open her arms to the poor and extend her hands to the needy. A woman who is set on honoring God with her life.

- How has being overly preoccupied with your body kept you from being a woman whose gaze, life, and heart are focused outward?

The Voice of Lies

We have a very real enemy, or spiritual adversary. I admit this kind of freaked me out when I first became a Christian, so I totally understand if you feel a bit skeptical, but bear with me, girl! I believe that this adversary's greatest attack against young women is to get us to strive for a false standard of beauty and to pursue that at all costs!

Satan is the master deceiver. Subtly he speaks lies that steer us away from the voice of truth. He knows that physical beauty is fleeting but that the strength of a woman who loves God is powerful and beyond measure. A preoccupation with food and body is an impediment to living the abundant life, and the enemy knows this. This is why he will do anything to keep our minds, hearts, and eyes fixed on our outer appearance.

- What are self-destructive thoughts you've believed? How have these lies of the enemy negatively influenced the way you relate to food or feel about your body and physical appearance?

Eating God's Way

Our hope is first and foremost that you will be healed and made whole from within by the love and grace of God. Our dream is that you will make peace with the body God has blessed you with and learn to approach food with freedom and confidence! We believe in this dream for you because we've seen it come true for so many girls!

Many people live in an unending fight, trying to tame and control their bodies. Years of abuse with over or undereating, stuffed emotions, and unrealistic expectations leave them feeling resentful, disgusted, and at disharmony with their bodies. But this is not how God intended us to live.

In an effort to eliminate this disharmony and walk on the path of an abundant life, we must be willing to befriend our bodies. Listening to the voice of God and giving your body what it needs sets you on the path toward reaching and maintaining your natural, God-given weight. Your natural weight is the size your body maintains when you eat according to your internal cues of hunger and fullness. Settling at your God-given weight is a process that takes practice, persistence, patience, and prayer.

So what does it mean to eat healthy—or to eat with God in mind? Eating God's way simply means:

- Eating between the boundaries of hunger and fullness. (Together we'll discover how!)
- Accepting food as a source of nourishment and sustenance.
- Going to God with your needs—not guys, food, retail therapy, or anything else to fill you emotionally and spiritually.
- Making wise food choices with the motive of being a good steward of the life and body God has given you.
- Obeying physiological hunger and the need for food rather than starving yourself or restricting your food intake.

my reflections

• How have you defined "healthy eating" in the past? How is your understanding of "healthy eating" similar or different from the *HEAL* definition?

Listen to Your Body

When you eat according to your internal hunger signals, you'll find that you eat smaller amounts of food. You'll need less food once you realize that much of your eating has been fueled by emotions. Food can't soothe or comfort our hungry souls, but God can. With God's help you will have the courage to listen to your body and obey your physiological need for food.

While on your *HEAL* Journey, you don't have to read food labels, count calories or fat grams, or restrict yourself to certain foods. You can embrace the foods you've told yourself you couldn't have—unless, of course, there's a medical reason to the contrary. (Just another reminder: Consult your doctor before beginning this journey.) We encourage you to have faith and trust that you can be your natural weight and still eat the foods you enjoy. Jesus tells us in Matthew 6:25: "Do not worry about your life, what you will eat or drink; or about your body, what you will wear. Is not life more important than food, and the body more important than clothes?"

All-or-Nothing Thinking Versus Balanced Thinking

Our understanding of eating is often linked to all-or-nothing thinking that looks something like this:

• I can only have 22 points a day.

• I can only eat organic foods.

• I have to ban all starches and refined foods from my diet.

This kind of thinking often backfires, leading to unhealthy eating! Have you found yourself eating huge amounts of "good" food in order to make up for your desire to have "bad" stuff, only to end up eating the "bad stuff" anyway? I know I have!

I shouldn't have that brownie. I'd really like to, but I can't because it's fattening. Alright…I'll just have a little piece. Ughhh! I blew it. I ate the whole thing, so I might as well eat the rest of them now. I'm such a pig. I'll never get over this.

Sound familiar? When we stop restricting foods from our diet and eat with the freedom we've been given in Christ, our desire for the foods we've denied ourselves lessens. We can allow ourselves to eat the very foods we fear the most. This process is scary, but it's a necessary step to living the abundant life.

Make a list of any foods you have banned from your diet or deemed "bad." Are there any foods that you currently restrict yourself from eating? If so, why?

- Foods I have banned:

_____

_____

- Foods I'm currently restricting from my list of acceptable foods:

_____

_____

- Why I have banned these foods from my life:

_____

_____

- Reflect on any occasions you have binged on the foods you listed above.

_____

_____

Maleah, a *HEAL* participant, said:

"Restriction is the worst thing you can do because it opens the doors for emotional binges. But when you know you can have anything you want, whenever you want it, you realize you don't have to stuff those doughnuts or brownies down your throat. You can have one today, and if tomorrow you want one, you can have another. I find that if I deny myself the things I really want, I end up rebelling and having them anyway but in huge amounts."

When we begin to allow ourselves to eat the very foods we have denied ourselves for so long, the intense desire for them gradually begins to fade. And with time, a piece of chocolate might eventually have less appeal to you on some days than a piece of fruit. When we surrender this simple area to God, he is able to equip us with a healthy, balanced perspective.

Practicing Balanced Thinking

Read the following examples of "all-or-nothing" thinking compared to balanced thinking. Then create scenarios of your own. Keep in mind that balanced thinking is realistic, flexible, and freedom-filled. "All-or-nothing" thinking is rigid, unforgiving, unrealistic, and self-destructive.

All	Balanced	Nothing
This week, I must do 45 minutes of cardio every day as well as three weight sessions.	*This week I have the freedom to take a friend on my favorite hike and enjoy a variety of classes at the gym.*	*I'll just sit around this week and not do much of anything since I totally failed last week.*
I'll eat absolutely no bread or starchy carbohydrates.	*I can have a piece of toast with breakfast if I'd like.*	*I might as well finish off the whole loaf of bread and have a doughnut while I'm at it.*
I have to do every single journal entry in this workbook.	*I can do as many entries as the Lord leads me to and complete it, if time permits.*	*I'm not even going to start the HEAL Journey because I'll completely fail like I have all the other times I've tried.*

- Where are you most likely to be "all or nothing" in your approach?

A Freedom-Filled Approach to Food!

I started my freshman year of college overweight. A serious encounter with depression caused me to take a year off after high school, and I gained nearly 40 pounds in a matter of months due in part to the medication I was prescribed. I went from being a fit, lean athlete to being overweight for the first time in my life. I spent months before my freshman year doing everything in my power to lose the excess weight I gained. I tried Weight Watchers, consumed the latest low-carb diet books, and exercised two hours a day. I would lose 10 pounds but quickly put them back on, only to do the same thing all over again. Still overweight by the end of my freshman year, I was exhausted and consumed by thoughts of food, and I went to see the nutritionist at my school's counseling center.

During our first session she took note of the foods I ate and didn't eat. I remember impressing her with my wealth of nutritional knowledge. I knew what the "good" foods and "bad" foods were, and I was confident in my intense exercise regimen that included training for a marathon, but I was humbled as I confessed how I would often eat emotionally and binge on all the foods I told myself I couldn't have.

After my first meeting she told me, "You need to stop denying yourself these foods." I remember thinking, *"What? Are you kidding?"* The thought of actually allowing myself to eat all the foods I considered "bad" was inconceivable. *"I'll gain 40 more pounds if I ever let myself eat that way,"* I thought. It went against everything I had read in my "health" magazines and the regimen I'd trained myself to follow.

But with time and her support, I began to follow her counsel. She helped me see that denying myself the "bad" foods I wanted actually led me to compulsively overeat, binge, and at times, even throw up. So with a lot of fear, I reluctantly allowed myself to have the foods I had "tried" to avoid. As I welcomed these foods back into my life,

my reflections

I had more peace and freedom and found that I wasn't bingeing or purging as I had before. I took my first step toward having a freedom-filled approach to food.

Accountability Moment

Remember, now's the time to call a girlfriend and share with her how things are going—and hear how she's doing, too.

The *HEAL* Pyramid

We've created the *HEAL* Pyramid as a visual that provides a clear picture of the direction you're headed. Each level of this pyramid represents a stage in your relationship to food, your body, and life.

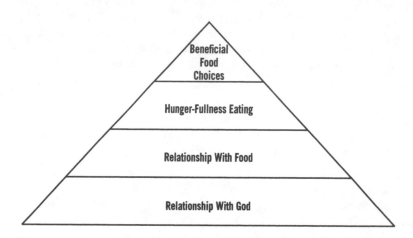

Relationship With God

The first level represents our foundation. Jesus taught about the importance of building on a firm foundation. In Matthew 7:24-27 he says: "Therefore everyone who hears these words of mine and puts them into practice is like a wise man who built his house on the rock. The rain came down, the streams rose, and the winds blew and beat against that house; yet it did not fall, because it had its foundation on the rock. But everyone who hears these words of mine and does not put them into practice is like a foolish man who built his house on sand. The rain came down, the streams rose, and the winds blew and beat against that house, and it fell with a great crash."

God is the rock we must cling to. He made us and knows us intimately, so it follows that he would know what's best for our bodies and how they've been designed to function. He's the foundation we must continually build upon if we truly want to cultivate a lasting friendship with food and our body.

Our spiritual needs are far more dominant than our physical needs. Mother Teresa said, "The hunger for love is much more difficult to remove than the hunger for bread." When God fashioned you in your mother's womb, he sculpted a heart-shaped hole within your soul that could only be filled by his love, intimacy, and presence.

We are a blessed but a very hungry generation of women. The people and things that we seek in order to feel loved will fail us. Our looks will fail us…food will fail us… guys, our family, and friends will fail us. But God never will. It's by daily drawing near to Jesus and embracing him as the One who can put us in right standing with God the Father that we are set upon the path of deep, authentic healing.

It's in relationship with God that we ultimately find the source of our true value and worth. As Judy says in her book *Thin Again,* "A solid sense of your identity and worth is the precursor to your ability to eat and live according to God's intent and being the person he designed you to be."

• What can you specifically do to make sure God is the foundation of your life as well as your *HEAL* Journey?

• Take some time to explore your heart. What is it hungry for?

my reflections

_____

_____

_____

_____

_____

_____

Relationship With Food

We all have a relationship with food. This level stands to both illustrate the difference between our spiritual and physical needs and also to encourage you to either cultivate or continue an emotionally healthy relationship with food.

Consider a young woman who is grappling with anorexia nervosa. For her to stay alive, it's imperative that her body receive physical nourishment. But beyond this need, there's a deeper hunger that is longing to be fed, a spiritual hunger that's yearning to be satisfied.

Janelle, another girl on the *HEAL* Journey, shares what she learned about the difference between her physical and spiritual needs:

Janelle's Story

"I was totally entrapped in my obsession to lose weight and severely restricted how much I ate. This obsession prevented me from investing time in my family, schoolwork, friendships, and my relationship with God.

"Since it was obvious that my health was wasting away, my parents and best friend finally confronted me. They expressed they didn't know what I was trying to do to myself, but that if I didn't stop, they were going to hospitalize me or send me somewhere to get professional help.

"I had to get to a point where I had nowhere to go. I could either continue on my path toward self-destruction and death—or I could let go and give it to God and just trust that he was going to be able to heal my heart and my mind. I knew that even if I started eating enough to keep my body alive, there was still something that neither food, nor doctors, nor anyone else would be able to fix.

"I finally had to give it up to God. I just sat down before him, broken and tired, and confessed my sin of being totally obsessed with losing weight. I cried out to God to heal me. 'God, I can't fix this problem. I just can't do it,' I told him. 'I need you to change my heart.' Once I went to God with all of my pain, my healing journey began."

• Take some time to reflect on the difference between your spiritual and physical needs.

Now that we've acknowledged the importance of our spiritual needs, let's uncover what it means to not just have a relationship with food but to have an *emotionally healthy* relationship with food. This has less to do with which foods you eat and more to do with the relationship you have with food. Your focus should be on allowing God to help you cultivate a peaceful, guilt-free, positive, and healthy relationship with food. Paul reminds us, "There is now no condemnation for those who are in Christ Jesus" (Romans 8:1).

The *HEAL* Journey is one of *progress,* not perfection. When we restrict certain foods, set unrealistic goals for ourselves, or engage in all-or-nothing thinking, we set ourselves up for failure. Remember, "It is for freedom that Christ has set us free. Stand firm, then, and do not let yourselves be burdened again by a yoke of slavery" (Galatians 5:1).

Hunger-Fullness Eating

The third level is "Hunger-Fullness Eating." This means eating between the boundaries of hunger and satisfaction. This stage is about abandoning any tendency to either overeat or undereat while learning to rely on the internal hunger and fullness cues God has given you. This concept is illustrated by the hunger-fullness chart, which can be used as a guide throughout the day.

Undereating					Healthy Eating						Overeating				
-5	-4	-3	-2	-1	0	1	2	3	4	5	6	7	8	9	10

Empty — Comfortable

Our hunger-fullness chart is divided into three sections. The middle range, "Healthy Eating," is scaled from 0 to 5, representing the range between hunger and satisfaction. Being "empty" or at a zero may be experienced by a growling sensation in your stomach or a slight burning sensation. It can also be an empty feeling within, which indicates a clear call for food. Prayerfully ask God to help you become aware of your body's messages and needs. In time you'll begin to determine when it is truly time to eat.

The range to the left represents undereating. If you've become accustomed to denying your physical hunger for extended periods of time, your body may not accurately decipher its true physiological need for food. In contrast, if you consistently eat beyond satisfaction (overeating), you can stretch your stomach to a point where it can accommodate more food than your body needs.

On this journey, common questions are, "What is the appropriate amount of food my stomach needs? How much food does my body need to go from a 0 to a 5?" To give you a better understanding of what your stomach actually needs when it's on empty, think of the size of your stomach as the size of your loosely-clenched fist. Thus, it takes about a loose fist-sized amount of pulverized (compacted by chewing) food to fill it up. Keep in mind; this is just a helpful visual. The density of the food you're eating also plays a big role in how much it fills you up. For example, salad will compact much more than a piece of steak.

Beneficial Food Choices

The fourth level entails welcoming natural and unprocessed foods into your daily food choices with thanksgiving, a pure heart, and in an emotionally healthy manner. The motive behind making beneficial food choices isn't simply to eat the "right" foods so you can have your ideal body. It's about making healthy food and lifestyle choices so you can live a long, vibrant life that brings God glory.

"The Lord does not look at the things man looks at. Man looks at the outward appearance, but the Lord looks at the heart" (1 Samuel 16:7).

Here is one girl's honest account:

Nina's Story

> *"After looking at the HEAL Pyramid, I realized that even though I was eating the best possible foods, I wasn't doing it in an emotionally healthy way. My motive wasn't to be a good caretaker of the body God has given me or to be healthy so I could love and serve the people in my life. My motivation was pretty selfish. I was trying to get super-skinny, have flawless skin, and be perceived as being 'perfect' by my friends.*
>
> *"Now I understand that God has so much more in mind for us. He cares for us—not only about our health and well-being—but about our hearts. God wants us to value the life he's given us and to know that those 'who have been given a trust must prove faithful' (1 Corinthians 4:2). He wants us to receive with a thankful heart the abundance of good, nutritious food we have at our disposal, and then to go and share our love and our lives with those in need. He wants us to be alive—to move beyond ourselves so that his light can shine through us to all people. I believe this is what the final stage in the HEAL Pyramid is really about. It means to have a spiritual approach to food and nutrition or to make beneficial choices."*

We move to a spiritually mature approach to nutrition when our spirit of vanity and perfectionism is replaced by a spirit of gratitude and a genuine desire to honor God. I think this comes only from a heart change—when we really realize who we are and who we belong to—that our lives, our beauty, and our bodies are not our own (1 Corinthians 6:19-20).

Pressing On

Where are you in your journey? Where do you feel God is leading you? Maybe you already have an emotionally healthy relationship with food but have yet to allow God to influence the way you eat and see your body. Perhaps you're trying to live a Christ-centered life but have damaged your body by drinking, smoking, or making poor nutritional choices. Wherever you are, take heart and believe that God longs to see you healed and made whole by his love and grace. May God be the rock that you cling to today as you continue your journey toward developing a healthy and positive approach to food, your body, and life.

Loving Father,

I praise you and thank you for the gift of my life, my body, and food. I ask that you reign in every area of my life. May you be my rock and my healer. Teach me what it means to eat healthy in your eyes. Help me to honor you with my body as you tenderly mold me in body, mind, and spirit into the woman you have created me to be. I rejoice that your strength is made perfect in my weakness and that in you I can do all things.

Amen.

Verse to Remember

"The Lord does not look at the things man looks at. Man looks at the outward appearance, but the Lord looks at the heart" (1 Samuel 16:7).

Free Space

Lesson 2: Group Study

The *HEAL* Basics

Opening

Read Psalm 139 together.

Recap

Discuss this past week's lesson. What resonated with you? What did God teach you through Lesson 2?

Sharing and Discussion

- Have you ever dieted? If so, what was that experience like?

- How is your previous concept of "healthy eating" similar or different from *HEAL*'s?

- When do you engage in all-or-nothing thinking?

- What lies about yourself have you believed?

- How have your accountability moments been going?

- What phase of the *HEAL* Pyramid do you need to grow in the most at this point on your journey?

Activity: Living Out the *HEAL* Pyramid—Your *HEAL* Goals

After discussing the *HEAL* Pyramid as a group, take some time individually to create personal *HEAL* goals for each level. Then list practical, action-oriented steps that will help you reach each of your goals. Remember that the Lord is not concerned with your outer appearance but with the motives of your heart. You can refer to the following example for guidance:

Level 2: Relationship With Food

Goal: To approach food with freedom, confidence, and peace, refraining from restrictive eating, emotional binges, and dieting.

Action Steps: To praise God and express gratitude for the food I am blessed to have by praying before each snack or meal. To throw away old diet books and begin to enjoy (in moderation) the foods I've denied myself in the past.

Level 1: Relationship With God

Goal:

_____

_____

_____

Action Steps:

_____

_____

_____

Level 2: Relationship With Food

Goal:

_____

_____

_____

Action Steps:

_____

_____

_____

Level 3: Hunger-Fullness Eating

Goal:

_____

_____

_____

Action Steps:

_____

_____

_____

Level 4: Beneficial Food Choices

Goal:

_____

_____

_____

Action Steps:

_____

_____

_____

Prayer

Take time to pray in smaller groups of two or three, asking God for the strength to accomplish these goals.

Lesson 3: Healing Your Hunger

Personal Study

God knows that we're a hungry generation of blessed but often broken women. He knows our potential to fully love and serve, but he also knows there are parts within us that are wounded. So he came to heal us and make us whole again.

We each have a hunger within our souls that craves to be fed—a hunger for love that longs to be satisfied. This "love hunger" is inherent within all of us, but it's how we respond to this hunger that determines the life we live. Will we allow *God* to fulfill the desires and hungers of our heart?

In John 4 Jesus speaks to a woman who was thirsty. As he traveled through Samaria, Jesus was tired and worn out, so he sat down to rest at a well. Open your Bible, read this story, and discover the powerful encounter that occurred between Jesus and this woman.

Take a moment to reflect on this account. Write your thoughts here.

_____

_____

_____

_____

_____

I long for the living water Jesus talks about. Don't we all? Our souls are thirsty and weary from striving. Exhausted and beaten down from searching, we discover that the world can't give us the living water our thirsty souls desire.

my reflections

What We Can Learn From This Story

Think about these truths drawn from the account in John 4. After each, write your thoughts about how this relates to your life and your journey toward healing.

• When we drink of this world, we will get thirsty again.

• To some Jesus may seem to be a stranger, yet he knows the most intimate aspects of us all, just as he did this Samaritan woman.

• Jesus is concerned about the details of our lives.

• There is a part of this woman in each of us. Just as she gave her heart away to many men, we may have given our hearts away to food, obsession with our physical appearance, guys, or something else.

• God offers us living water—he offers us eternal life! We're reminded that this life isn't all there is.

Hungry Hearts

I love how Judy addresses the matter of heart hunger in her book *Thin Again*.

"If we will be still and let God address our silent hunger, he will graciously show us that he never meant for us to find the fulfillment of our self-worth apart from him. This undeniable, unavoidable longing for a sense of value is a sanctified hunger placed in us by God's design, but we will never experience inner peace until we face the truth that nothing of this world—our appearance, our performance, others' opinions of us, or our past experience—can fulfill our longing for security and significance."

As much as we try to avoid it or control it, hunger—both physical and spiritual—is a *good* thing. It is a constant reminder of how dependent we are on God to meet our every need. Our hunger gives us a continuous opportunity to draw near to the One who is our comfort and source of life.

- What is your heart hungry for?

- How has your need for security and significance not been met? How have you responded to this loss?

- How have you relied on food, or an intentional lack of food, to comfort you?

Healing Our Heartaches

For some of us, our heart hunger has been awakened by abuse, hurtful words, painful experiences, tragedy, absent parents, or…I'll let you fill in the blank. Often we are hurt by people we love or by intruders who have trespassed into our lives. No matter how big or small we perceive these heartaches to be, they are no small matter to God. For us to become free of our brokenness, we must be able to acknowledge our heartaches and give them to God.

We cannot experience permanent authentic healing apart from God. And we cannot get past these hurts by relying on something other than God. Judy says, "By focusing on externals—our diets, our weight, our eating or not eating—we avoid confronting the real issues in our lives: our fears, unresolved grief, emotions, relationships, rebellion, and insecurities."

Who or what has hurt you the most? Ask God to reveal how these people or experiences have affected your life.

_____

_____

_____

_____

my reflections

my reflections

_____

_____

_____

Know My Heart

"Search me, O God, and know my heart; test me and know my anxious thoughts. See if there is any offensive way in me, and lead me in the way everlasting" (Psalm 139:23-24).

Girls, if there's going to be any real change in our lives, this has to be our genuine request to God. Before we're transformed physically, we must be refined and renewed from within. That's what the *HEAL* Journey is about—going to God daily and asking him to search our hearts, to test us, and to make us more inwardly beautiful in his sight. It's about transformation from the inside out. As God brings to light the things that are not pleasing to him, we are presented with the opportunity to become the women he wants us to be.

We bring our utter brokenness and humanity while God provides us with his redemptive power, his redeeming love, and his healing grace. It is in this quiet place of surrender, when we lay our brokenness before him, that God mysteriously works in our lives and changes our hearts.

The prayer in Psalm 139 caused me to ask God, "What's offensive and ugly in my life? What do I do that bums you out?" Of course there are a lot of things I do that must hurt God's heart, but when I think about specific offenses on my journey, this list comes to mind: idolatry, hatred, envy, and selfish ambition—all of which are mentioned in Galatians 5:19-21. Let me break these down:

- *Idolatry:* Idolizing what I think is the ideal body and women who I feel have it!
- *Hatred:* Disliking and criticizing the way I've been made.

- *Envy:* Coveting the beauty of other women while failing to see the beauty my Creator sees in me, his beloved.
- *Selfish ambition:* Focusing on *me*! Fixating on my body, my weight, food, etc. Vanity! Forgetting the abundant life of joy, love, service, faith, and friendship, which I have been created to enjoy.

Use these questions to probe your own heart:

- When do I run to tangible things instead of God for comfort? What are those things?

- Do I listen to truth, or do I allow anxious thoughts to reign in my mind?

- When am I most likely to affirm myself, and when am I most likely to be self-condemning?

- Do I judge others by the shape or size of their bodies or by what they eat or wear?

- What's my focus? What do I think about during the day?

- Do I praise God for the ability to exercise and enjoy my body, or am I preoccupied with my weight?

- Do I spend time daily in prayer? Do I read and memorize Bible verses or take time to reflect on the truth of God's Word?

- How pure and edifying are the things I expose myself to such as friends, music, Internet, television, magazines, movies, and so on?

my reflections

my reflections

_____

_____

_____

_____

_____

_____

_____

_____

_____

_____

_____

_____

_____

_____

_____

_____

_____

_____

_____

_____

_____

_____

_____

_____

_____

_____

> ### Accountability Moment
>
> *Remember, now's the time to call a girlfriend and share with her how things are going—and hear how she's doing, too.*

The Three Types of Hunger

Healthy Eating and Abundant Living recognizes three types of hunger—head hunger, heart hunger, and stomach hunger. When we eat in response to these hungers, we either engage in desire eating, emotional eating, or healthy eating, respectively. Let's look at each more closely.

Head Hunger

Head hunger is associated with a compulsion to eat or indulge in a certain food that looks appealing when your body isn't hungry. When you act upon your head hunger, you're engaging in "desire eating" and are yielding to the strong desire to eat food that appeals to you visually and purely for the pleasure it brings.

Head hunger is common for every human whose taste buds and senses are up and running, so don't freak out! It's totally normal to experience head hunger. For example, your grandma bakes a batch of the world's best white-macadamia nut cookies just for you; you walk by the local Starbucks and that Mocha Frappuccino screams your name.

As you ask God to help you navigate how to respond to head hunger, trust that he'll give you discernment. He may give a woman who struggles with undereating the discernment that it's helpful for her healing to eat when she experiences head hunger, while he may convict someone who struggles with overeating otherwise.

If your struggle relates to eating more food than your body needs, be honest with yourself about head hunger, and ask the following questions:

- How often do I give in to my head hunger?

- How much do I eat at those times?

- Does it cause me to go overboard and binge?

- How do I feel afterward—physically, emotionally, and spiritually?

- Are there specific foods that I choose to eat when giving in to head hunger?

Head hunger can separate us from God, especially if we overindulge. And if you're overweight, consistently eating from head hunger (instead of stomach hunger) will prevent you from reaching your natural weight, which is the weight God created you to be.

On the other hand, if you've been captive to restrictive eating, give yourself the freedom to eat what looks good to you. This is especially true as you are relearning how to eat. Some women have suppressed their physical hunger to the point that they no longer are able to feel hunger even when their body is in dire need of sustenance.

Heart Hunger

Heart hunger is a compulsion to mismanage our feelings and emotional moods with food. We often don't recognize that we're allowing our emotions and feelings to drive us to food. When you act upon heart hunger, you're engaging in emotional eating, which can be triggered by any emotion, such as anger, sadness, frustration, or loneliness. Emotional highs and lows are inevitable; it's part of being human. However, what we do with our emotions and how we manage them determines whether or not we'll be controlled by them.

my reflections

After identifying your hunger as heart hunger, pinpoint the emotion(s) you're experiencing. Here are some of the most common feelings we experience:

- Boredom
- Apathy
- Tiredness
- Anger
- Loneliness
- Sadness
- Frustration
- Nervousness
- Anxiety
- Being overwhelmed

Keep in mind that we can try to satisfy our heart hunger with things other than food: excessive shopping, guys, TV, incessantly calling or texting friends, compulsive activities, or searching for excitement online. Instead, God must be our ultimate refuge.

Stomach Hunger

Stomach hunger is usually recognized by a growling sensation or a slight burning sensation in your stomach. When you obey your stomach hunger and eat until you find a comfortable point between hunger and fullness, you are engaging in healthy eating.

If you struggle with anorexic tendencies, you probably err on the side of not eating enough food. You might think that the amount of food you've chosen to eat is sufficient, when in reality it's not. Anorexia is a serious condition where professional help is advisable.

If you struggle with overeating, remember how easy it is to choose more food than your body really needs. With this in mind, you can courageously begin to select smaller portions.

Some people might swing between both sides of the spectrum—from severely restricting themselves to bingeing or even purging. Be aware of what side of the spectrum you tend to err on in terms of disordered eating. Being self-aware is the first step toward making positive changes.

Rate your physical (stomach) hunger according to the *HEAL* Hunger and Fullness Scale. As we discussed in Lesson 2, "healthy eating" ranges from 0 to 5, which is a visual aid for you to numerically identify your current hunger level.

As you obey your God-given hunger and fullness signals and ignore head hunger by going to God with your emotions, he will faithfully bring you to the healthy, natural size he created you to be.

Hunger and Fullness Scale

Undereating					Healthy Eating					Overeating				
-5	-4	-3	-2	-1	0	1	2	3	4	5	6	7	8	9	10
					Empty					Comfortable				

Lauren, a college student, shares how God has helped heal her hungers:

Lauren's Story

"When I went away to college, it was a scary and a very unsure time in my life. I was away from my family, my home, and everything I had grown up with. Being introduced to cafeteria food was one of the biggest transitions I experienced. I was feeling very vulnerable, so every time I ate at the cafeteria, I filled up on foods that were not the healthiest choices. I did this for instant comfort and would often eat past my "full" mark. Because I was limited to three meals a day at the cafeteria, usually I ate more than I normally would have at home...just in case I got hungry later. The worst part about overeating was the guilty feelings afterward that made me feel horrible.

"This went on until I was introduced to Wonderfully Made, through which I found the HEAL Program, and came to the realization that the Lord wanted to be involved in my eating...I was able to see my body just as God saw it, and it was then that I gave my heart and head hunger to him. My prayer before each meal was for the Lord to help me eat only as much as my body needed and to stop when I was comfortable. Before beginning my HEAL Journey, I thought I was doomed to stuffing myself on cafeteria food for the rest of my college years, but God showed me that he is the center of that part in my life."

Navigating Your Hungers

While you definitely need physical nourishment when your body has been denied food, you also need to be spiritually nourished. So ask God to open your heart to his presence and power as you pray and feed on his Word. Invite the Lord into your struggle, and surrender the deeper hungers of your heart to him. Ask God for the willingness to relinquish control, and trust him with your needs while you obey as he directs.

- List times within the past week when you ate outside of true, physiological hunger (if this applies to you). Where were you and what were you doing? What were you thinking or feeling? Were you with people or were you alone? What, and how much, did you eat? How did you feel afterward?

my reflections

- List any times recently when you may have intentionally denied your stomach hunger and did not eat even though you were hungry.

Eating Without Fear and Eating With Freedom

Jesus said, "I tell you the truth, everyone who sins is a slave to sin" (John 8:34). Do you want to be a slave to food? You have the choice to remain a slave to food or to be set free. When you submit to head hunger or heart hunger or starve yourself, you're giving food the upper hand over your life. Yet food has absolutely no power over us unless we *give* it that power.

Our relationship with food and eating is meant to be a source of appropriate enjoyment and nourishment. But it can be a weapon with which we punish ourselves—either by denying ourselves food or overstuffing ourselves. Ask God to free you from this area of bondage. Have hope! There's freedom in eating God's way!

Two Steps Forward, One Step Back

Be gentle with yourself on this journey toward healthy eating and awesome living, and remember it's just that—*a journey*! Keep these words from Philippians 3:12-14 in mind as an encouragement: "Not that I have already obtained all this, or have already been made perfect, but I press on to take hold of that for which Christ Jesus took hold of me. Brothers, I do not consider myself yet to have taken hold of it. But one thing I do: Forgetting what is behind and straining toward what is ahead, I press on toward the goal to win the prize for which God has called me heavenward in Christ Jesus."

The Super-Practical Steps of Healthy Eating

Let's put what we've been talking about into seven simple steps that can help us eat mindfully.

my reflections

Step 1: Select When to Eat

Get in touch with your hunger and satisfaction cues. Learning how to gauge your hunger and fullness is a process, so give yourself some time. Use the hunger scale regularly throughout the day.

Step 2: Select What to Eat

Choose food that will both satisfy and nourish you.

Step 3: Sit Down

If you think you don't have time to actually sit down and enjoy your meal, then take a closer look at your life, and figure out a way to *make* the time! Sitting down while you eat facilitates digestion and also enables you to relax and more fully enjoy your food.

Step 4: Say Thanks

Most of us are blessed to have access to food whenever we want, so it's a privilege to cultivate a heart of gratefulness. Talk to God with a thankful heart for the food he has provided. Ask him to guide you as you eat so that you can respond appropriately to your body's signals of hunger and satisfaction. Finally, ask him to nourish you with the food so you can serve him.

Step 5: Slow Down and Take Small Bites

Don't engage in "garbage disposal eating": throwing it in, grinding it up, and sucking it down. Take deep, slow breaths; put your fork down; and enjoy your food and the people sharing the meal with you.

Step 6: Savor the Flavor

While food should never be something we worship, it's certainly not wrong for us to enjoy it! Savor the food you eat—enjoy the sight, smell, and taste.

Step 7: Satisfy!

Stop eating when you feel satisfied—not when you're so full that you have to lie horizontally! Remember, there is a 20- to 30-minute delay before your brain registers that you are pleasantly satisfied.

> **Memory Verse**
>
> *"Everything is permissible for me"—but not everything is beneficial. "Everything is permissible for me"—but I will not be mastered by anything. "Food for the stomach and the stomach for food"—but God will destroy them both (1 Corinthians 6:12-13).*

my reflections

Free Space

Lesson 3: Group Study

Healing Your Hunger

Opening

Read Psalm 139 together.

Recap

Discuss this past week's lesson. What resonated with you? What did God teach you? What stood out in the writings? Take some time to discuss what you learned in Lesson 3.

Activity—Being the Woman at the Well

Close your eyes and take some time to quiet your thoughts and your heart as you imagine that you are the woman at the well.

It's been a long, hot day, and you are tired from hours of working. Thirsty and hot, you go to the well to draw some water. When you arrive at the well, you find a man there you've never seen before. He's a stranger, yet there's something so familiar about him that you're unafraid. He has a quiet strength about him that comforts you.

He asks you for a drink. What do you say?

He tells you something about yourself that only you would know. What is this secret of yours that he mentions?

You discover that this man is Jesus. How do you respond?

He tells you that water from the well will leave you thirsty again, but says that if you would ask him for water, he would give you living water—a well of water that will spring up into everlasting life.

What else does he want to tell you?

Share your thoughts and reflections with a partner as you are comfortable.

Activity

With one or two other girls, describe what you experience when you encounter each type of hunger. What thoughts accompany each type of hunger? Next, record how you respond when you experience that particular type of hunger.

Type of Hunger	What emotions or feelings do you experience?	What thoughts do you experience?	How do you respond to this hunger?
Heart Hunger			
Head Hunger			
Stomach Hunger			

Sharing and Discussion

- What is one of the heartaches you've experienced in your life, and how did you respond to this heartache?

- What kind of "heart" hunger do you most frequently encounter, and how have you usually dealt with it?

- How do you think your "heart" hunger can be filled?

- Are there any other heartaches God wants to heal in you?

Lesson 4: Body Beautiful

Personal Study

Being wonderfully made entails being body beautiful:

We have arms to hug

Feet to travel upon

Eyes to discover

Ears to listen

A mouth to taste

Lips to kiss

Hands to serve

A smile to share

A heart to love

Regardless of the number on the scale, what size jeans you wear, or whether you have 10 fingers and 10 toes, you are a beautiful masterpiece, a work of art, created by God. You are body beautiful!

It's a challenge to view our bodies from such a spiritual perspective while constantly being bombarded by the standards of a materialistic world. As if our personal expectations for ourselves aren't unforgiving enough, we place our bodies against the narrow measurements of whatever the media affirms as perfect and desirable.

- What expectations have you placed on yourself and your body?

- How have your words or actions placed expectations upon other women?

my reflections

• Where do you think these expectations have come from?

If we're going to live full and fabulous lives, we have to do away with the idealistic and what's "just not right" for the *wonderfully made* woman God has created you to be. Maybe a certain model's frame is right for the way God made her, but it may not be the way God designed you. And that's got to be OK if we choose God's perspective on beauty instead of the world's ideal. We all have our "perfect" imperfections, and that's what being body beautiful is all about.

Let's go back to Psalm 139. In verse 14, David tells God, "I praise you because I am fearfully and wonderfully made." David does not applaud himself for his individual design nor does he criticize God's work. He gives God praise for the work he has made. David continues, "Your works are wonderful, I know that full well." He doesn't say, "Hey, God—you know you kinda messed up on me. I mean, my toes look funny; I'm kind of short and..." *Definitely not!* David recognizes the brilliance of his Creator and shouts out genuine praise and thanksgiving. Let's aspire to have hearts filled with praise for the awesome and unique way God has made each of us.

Paul makes the same point when he says, "But who are you, O man, to talk back to God? 'Shall what is formed say to him who formed it, "Why did you make me like this?" ' " (Romans 9:20). Let's not dishonor God by condemning his creation.

David's words in Psalm 139:13 can help us learn how to view our bodies from a spiritual rather than worldly perspective. He says, "For you created my inmost being; you knit me together in my mother's womb." The truth is so important for us girls to grasp: God took his time in creating us; he labored over our design and formed us uniquely out of a divine love that is permanently imprinted on every cell in our body.

One of the best ways to learn how to walk in the truth that you are body beautiful is to talk to God about it. Ask God to help you see yourself through his eyes rather than through the eyes of the world. If you want to love your body, you have to fall in love with the One who made it! Go to God, your Maker, and ask him to help you begin to see your body as:

- His wonderfully made creation

- Proof of God's glory

- An instrument of his love and service

- A powerful force on the earth

- The temple of the Holy Spirit

Set aside time to reflect on what it means for a baby to be knit within its mother's womb. It's a miracle beyond words. God, our Father and Creator, knit *you* together in your mother's womb. And he foreknew a loving future for you—one filled with adventure, wonderful plans, and an irreplaceable role that only you can fill. You have been in his hands since the day he first thought of you, and you will be forever.

Benchmarking

If you're unsure whether or not you're in a healthy weight range, we suggest you talk to your doctor. Your doctor can give you the necessary insight to determine whether or not it's advisable for you to gain or lose weight. Many of you may already be in a healthy weight range, which can be helpful for a doctor to confirm to you—especially when you desire to lose unnecessary weight.

For example, if a medical professional informs someone that she is actually 5-10 pounds underweight (according to healthy weight ranges relative to her height), and she has believed she needs to lose weight, this information may offer the insight to open her eyes to the fact that there are deeper issues that need to be addressed. This knowledge can possibly help her relinquish her obsession to lose weight and instead highlight the spiritual and heart issues at the core of this obsession in a way that encourages her to enter into a more intimate relationship with God.

my reflections

In the same way, if a medical professional informs someone else that her weight falls in the overweight category, it is important for her to acknowledge the health risks associated with being overweight—especially diabetes and heart disease. Coming to grips with this fact can be instrumental in her decision to pursue physical health and emotional and spiritual healing.

It can be helpful for you to benchmark where you are now, or to know whether or not you are at a healthy weight range as this knowledge can give you insight to move forward on your journey. It can help give you direction as you learn to make peace with your body and choose a life of health.

Writing Your Body Vision Statement

A body vision statement is a sentence or two that captures in words the place of peace and reconciliation you want to arrive at with your body. It encompasses the physical, spiritual, and emotional aspects of your relationship with your body in light of your relationship with God.

A body vision statement is like a compass, providing you with focus, truth, and clarity for your unique food and body challenges. Ask yourself a series of questions in light of anything new God may have revealed to you. Ask yourself, "Is it God's best plan for me to release weight, gain weight, or accept and embrace my current weight?" Note that the body vision statements like the ones listed below are Christ-centered, future-oriented, and simple.

- *To make peace with and cherish my body as it is now, believing fully that it is healthy and beautiful, thereby having the freedom I need to fix my eyes upon the greater things of God.*

- *To live in freedom and confidence with my body at its healthy weight range so I can powerfully love and serve the people in my life.*

- *To allow God to instill within me a sense of his love and acceptance for my body, giving me the strength I need to be liberated from the bondage of being overweight and displeased with the gift of my body.*

- *To cultivate an accurate perception of my body and relinquish any self-criticism or fear of weight gain so that God can shape the life of adventure, beauty, and service he has for me.*

Now write your own body vision statement. If you are willing, share it with your group when you meet.

┌───┐
│   │
│   *My Body Vision Statement*   │
│   │
│   │
│   │
│   │
│   │
│   │
│   │
│   │
│   │
│   │
└───┘

my reflections

_____

_____

_____

_____

_____

_____

_____

_____

_____

_____

_____

_____

_____

_____

_____

_____

_____

_____

_____

_____

Your Body's a Temple

"Do you not know that your body is a temple of the Holy Spirit, who is in you, whom you have received from God? You are not your own; you were bought at a price. Therefore honor God with your body" (1 Corinthians 6:19-20).

This passage reveals an important truth. If we have welcomed God into our lives then our bodies are not our own! If we are God's girls, then his Holy Spirit resides within our physical bodies. And if God's Spirit is in us, then our bodies are like the Temple in Old Testament times. This temple—your body—is a holy and a very sacred place, a place inhabited by God that is intended to be used to worship and honor him. Ephesians 1:13 confirms this: "And you also were included in Christ when you heard the word of truth, the gospel of your salvation. Having believed, you were marked in him with a seal, the promised Holy Spirit, who is a deposit guaranteeing our inheritance until the redemption of those who are God's possession—to the praise of his glory."

- Are you treating your body as the holy and sacred place it is, or are you destroying it with your choices and actions?

- How do you view your body? Do you see your body as a wonderfully made creation that belongs to God?

- Do you criticize and belittle your body with harsh words and contempt? Or do you treat it with a spirit of encouragement and acceptance?

- How do you nurture and care for yourself? Do you get enough sleep? Do enjoy nutritious foods and adequate exercise?

- Do you damage God's temple with cigarettes, drugs, inappropriate sexual behavior, or excessive alcohol?

Your body belongs to our heavenly Father. It is his dwelling place, and we must treat our body as the holy place it is.

Our Whole Being

God wants you to offer your whole being—heart, soul, mind, body, gifts, talents, experiences, and knowledge—for his purposes. Romans 6:13 says, "Do not offer the parts of your body to sin, as instruments of wickedness, but rather offer yourselves to God, as those who have been brought from death to life; and offer the parts of your body to him as instruments of righteousness." Those "parts of your body" include your smile, arms, legs, laughter, hands, ears, eyes, nose, voice. How awesome it is to think that Jesus is alive in us and uses our whole being if we have asked him into our lives.

Contrary to what the world says, your body is not just something to be looked at and adorned. Its purpose is to serve, encourage, and love the people we encounter. Girls, it's time we discover and reclaim the true, God-given purpose of our bodies. When you get to heaven, God isn't going to ask what size jeans you wore, how many magazines you posed for, or how many boys you dated. What *will* matter to him is how many people you hugged, how many tears you wiped away, how many smiles you gave, and how many aching hearts you touched with his love.

Accountability Moment

Remember, now's the time to call a girlfriend and share with her how things are going—and hear how she's doing, too.

Body Stewardship

Our energy, talents, opportunities, relationships, resources, health, intelligence, and time on earth have been entrusted to us by God—they belong to him and we are to be good stewards (or managers) of what belongs to him. To honor God, we must care for and manage these to the best of our abilities, both spiritually and physically.

Spiritual Stewardship

Spiritual stewardship means that we remind ourselves (and one another!) of our body's reality—that it is not our own, that it is precious and sacred, and that it is the temple of the Holy Spirit. Embrace the meaning of being fearfully and wonderfully made! Walk in the truth that you're God's beautiful creation, and shut out the voices that give you a worldly perspective of the human figure.

Girls, let's read those "beauty" magazines less and God's Word more; look less at appearance and more at one's character; spend less time criticizing and focusing on our bodies and more time using them to serve others.

Physical Stewardship

Physical stewardship means doing our best to be the natural and healthy weight God intended. The desire to be our natural weight is inherent in most of us. We function much better, both physically and emotionally, when our bodies are at our God-given size.

Part of being wonderfully made means that we've been made with a purpose. Being significantly overweight *or* underweight can make it more difficult, emotionally and physically, to execute this purpose to our full potential. Being outside the boundary of your healthy body state often means that you may not be managing the gift of your body as best you can. If you're significantly above or below your natural weight, you will not have the energy, health, and stamina to function well and live effectively for Jesus. If it's your hope to accomplish what God's put you here to do, whether it's being a mom, a high-powered CEO, a singer, an amazing friend, or all of the above, it's going to be hard to be effective without the physical stamina God intends you to have.

Physical stewardship also means getting regular exercise. I truly believe that exercise is an essential part of living a full and fabulous life. Exercise brings many positives: self-confidence, energy, a healthy heart, an enhanced mood, better health, peaceful sleep, an improved ability to fight infections, and this list goes on! Exercise helps keep us healthy and fit for serving God and others.

Let's encourage one another not to limit exercise to the gym, the treadmill, or the track. Get wild! Be creative! Go for a swim, hike a nearby hill, power walk with friends, work out with a Pilates tape, join a pickup game of soccer, take the stairs, go surfing, do adult gymnastics, dance! Whatever exercise you choose, make it fun, make it doable, and make it something you can integrate into your life for years to come! Just think of all the awesome things a healthy, vibrant body can let you do: camp under the stars, jump off a waterfall, swim in the ocean, backpack Europe, play sports with your best friends, be a playful mother, laugh aloud, give hugs, lend a hand, ride a bike, create a garden, decorate a home with loving care.

My Exercise Ideas

my reflections

_____
_____
_____
_____
_____
_____
_____
_____
_____
_____
_____
_____
_____
_____
_____
_____
_____
_____
_____
_____

Call someone who is joining you on the *HEAL* Journey, and plan a fun, physical activity together for the week!

List your plans here and follow through:

Exercise buddy: _____

Play date: _____

Type of activity: _____

I pray that your time will be blessed—that you and your friend will be reminded of the fun-loving, little girls inside each of you as you enjoy the gift of exercise and friendship.

Giving Thanks

Gratitude is not something God gives us. It's a gift we can give to him for all the blessings we've been given. I encourage you to cultivate gratitude for the body God has blessed you with—deep, pervading, constant gratitude. Gratitude comes from a true understanding of how blessed and beautiful we are despite our perceived imperfections. Even though we may experience moments of self-criticism and disappointment regarding our bodies, we owe our wonderful Maker thanks for the gift of life and the body we've been given.

Love Your Body First

We must learn to love and appreciate our bodies first before we look to someone else to find it beautiful. Love for your body opens the door for others to find your body worthy of respect. Like laughter, how you feel about your body is contagious. If you carry yourself and your body in a way that communicates confidence, security, and contentment, others will get this vibe and reciprocate this respect.

If you're blessed to become a mother or a mentor someday, you'll have the opportunity to teach your daughter (or encourage another girl) to be confident in her own skin, even though some of our moms or mentors may not have been able to do that for us.

As a friend you can model to your girlfriends how to love and find beauty in their own bodies by finding beauty in your own. If you walk and talk like the beautiful daughter of God that you are, you can free the women around you from a negative self-image, too. How can we expect our boyfriends, husbands, children, and friends to cherish us if *we* don't see ourselves as worthy? God has already called your body "good." He wants you to believe this truth and communicate it to the world around you. So walk tall and carry your body like the temple of God it is. If we are going to change the ways of this world, it has to start with us.

- What message have you communicated about your body to your friends and family?

- In what ways has your mom or other women close to you (such as a mentor, coach, or friends) affected the way you feel about your body?

Your Body Beautiful Checklist

A while ago, I realized that there were days or moments when I would feel great in my own skin, but there were other times when that wasn't the case. After reflecting on this change of perspective, I was able to pinpoint some of the things that often influenced how I felt about my body and realized there were tangible things I could do to bring my body image back into alignment with God's truth. It is so important to keep our body confidence in check because the way we feel about ourselves can often trigger emotionally unhealthy eating habits or other forms of self-destructive behavior.

Here's what I call a Body Beautiful Checklist. This is a list of beneficial actions that can help us feel positively about our bodies. Add to this list or edit it as you see fit.

❑ I ate between my natural signals of hunger and fullness.

my reflections

❑ I engaged in exercise that I enjoyed.

❑ I refrained from looking at fashion magazines, media images, or from envying other women's bodies.

❑ I affirmed myself and my body by meditating on God's truth.

❑ I took care of my body by getting enough rest and making beneficial food choices.

❑ I set aside an unhealthy habit.

❑

❑

❑

❑

Prayer

Lord,

I thank you that I am made in your image and likeness. I praise you because I am fearfully and wonderfully made. Help me to see myself not through my eyes or those of the world, but through yours. How wonderful is the love you have lavished upon me, that you have called me your child.

Amen.

Questions

• How can you daily remind yourself that your body is a temple of the Holy Spirit?

• What changes in your life do you need to make in order to better honor God with your body?

Challenge

Shower yourself with affirmations that will help you develop a healthy relationship with your body and encourage you to build your body image in God, not in the world. Feel free to write them below:

_____

_____

_____

_____

Memory Verse

"Do you not know that your body is a temple of the Holy Spirit, who is in you, whom you have received from God? You are not your own; you were bought at a price. Therefore honor God with your body" (1 Corinthians 6:19-20).

Free Space

Lesson 4: Group Study

Body Beautiful

Opening

Read Psalm 139 together.

Recap

Discuss this past week's lesson. What resonated with you? What did God teach you? Is there anything that stood out? Discuss what you learned.

Activity

Take turns sharing your Body Vision Statements with one another.

Quiet yourself as a group. Turn down the lights, put on soft music, and enter into a period of silence. As your heart and mind are quieted and you enter into God's peace, share praises about your body before one another and before God. Tell him what you are thankful for and what you love and appreciate about your body and what it enables you to do.

Sharing and Discussion

• Share a beneficial action you added to your "Body Beautiful Checklist"?

my reflections

_____

_____

_____

_____

_____

_____

_____

_____

_____

_____

_____

_____

_____

_____

_____

_____

_____

_____

_____

• How has your body allowed you to serve others? How can you continue to serve in the future?

• What message have you communicated about your body to others?

• How have important women in your life affected the way you feel about your body?

• How do you talk about your body in front of your friends or loved ones?

• How can you change any negative messages you have communicated about your body to others?

Prayer

Close your time praying together either one-on-one or as a group.

Lesson 5: An Aisle of Grace

Personal Study

I think we miss out on the full character of God unless we are fully able to grasp the true meaning of *grace*. Defined as "God's free and unmerited favor for sinful humanity," grace is the lovingkindness of God made real in our lives. His favor is upon us always, not just sometimes.

Grace frees us to walk in the truth that *nothing* can separate us from God's love. Our performance cannot; our brokenness cannot, nor can our pride or lack of self-worth. Embracing his boundless love frees us from our self-imposed performance-based prisons. God's grace and love are not based on what or how much we eat or on how often we exercise.

Self-love and worldly acceptance measured by how we follow man-made rules are standards we can never meet. Upon assessing our performance at the end of the day (what we ate or didn't eat, how little we exercised, and so on), we'll often fall short. And when we feel we don't measure up, we conclude that we aren't worthy to be loved.

But God's love is not rigid and unforgiving like the love we often grant ourselves. To some of us, this love is irrational. We may think that his love must be earned or that we must prove ourselves worthy to receive it. As Brennan Manning said, "How long will it be before we discover we cannot dazzle God with our accomplishments? When will we acknowledge that we need not and cannot buy God's favor? When will we acknowledge that we don't have it all together and happily accept the gift of grace?"

- Have you ever tried to "dazzle" God or others with your accomplishments? If so, how?

my reflections

Many young women today are raised feeling pressured to walk upon a tightrope of perfection. We cling desperately to this tightrope, afraid of losing control or not measuring up. We may be able to maintain our balance on this tightrope for a while, but eventually we'll fall and get hurt. The tightrope of perfection is unrealistic and not of God. God wants us to take our gaze away from this high, dangerous place and to call out for him to rescue us. Whenever we call out to him, he is quick to catch us and set our feet safely upon the path of his grace, love, and provision. It's upon this path, this "aisle of grace," that we're led to the abundant life he desires for his beloved daughters.

David acknowledged the grace of God in Psalm 18:36, "You broaden the path beneath me, so that my ankles do not turn." God does not want us to stumble or fall as a result of the pressure that we, or others, place upon ourselves. I pray that you will have the courage to live in the freedom contained in God's grace.

- Have you ever felt pressured to walk on a tightrope of perfection? If so, how did you respond?

The aisle of grace in your *HEAL* Journey means it's OK on occasion to eat past a 5 or to forego your regular exercise plans. You're loved regardless of your performance and what you have or have not accomplished. Jesus' love is constant and ever present. Hebrews 13:8 says, "Jesus Christ is the same yesterday and today and forever." Romans 8:35 and 38-39 give us assurance of God's love, saying, "Who shall separate us from the love of Christ? Shall trouble or hardship or persecution or famine or nakedness or danger or sword?...For I am convinced that neither death nor life, neither angels nor demons, neither the present nor the future, nor any powers, neither height nor depth, nor anything else in all creation, will be able to separate us from the love of God that is in Christ Jesus our Lord."

- When do you feel most separated from the love of God? from the love of others?

- How has such a loss or perceived loss of love influenced your thoughts, self-image, relationships, and possibly even your approach to food, eating, and your body?

- How does the love you receive from your heavenly Father compare with the love you experience from other people in your life?

Legalism Versus Grace

Today's diets and self-help plans are often rooted in legalism. They're built on a set of rules designed to govern and control our behavior. The problem with legalism is that it does nothing to change us from within or heal our hearts. In *Thin Within,* Judy says, "Legalism says that we must shape up by adhering to fixed formulas or a rigid set of laws or codes. This is a deception, however, because no external constraint (legalism) can satisfy our need for love and intimacy, nor can it create a pure heart."

In the following passage Paul reminds us of this fact:

"Since you died with Christ to the basic principles of this world, why, as though you still belonged to it, do you submit to its rules: 'Do not handle! Do not taste! Do not touch!'? These are all destined to perish with use, because they are based on human commands and teachings. Such regulations indeed have an appearance of wisdom, with their self-imposed worship, their false humility and their harsh treatment of the body, but they lack any value in restraining sensual indulgence" (Colossians 2:20-23).

I love this passage because it's so right on! When it comes to food, how many times have we told ourselves: "Do not handle! Do not touch!" Rigid rules have nothing to do with things of eternal value and certainly nothing to do with our salvation. We think that following these regulations will somehow make us wise or worthy, but in reality they don't address our hungry hearts or make us feel loved. As followers of Jesus, we have died to the ways of the world! This means that we must put to death the world's views about food, exercise, our body, and eating. Let our minds be renewed with the truth that God has revealed to us through his Word and actively apply it to our lives.

- What legalistic rules or regulations have you imposed upon yourself in regard to eating, exercise, and your body?

my reflections

• What was the source of those self-imposed rules?

• What do you think might be some barriers to experiencing God's love?

Freedom That Conforms

Many of us have been profoundly influenced by the self-imposed command "I have to." You might tell yourself, "I have to abstain from this particular food," or "I have to exercise seven times a week or I'm a failure." Where's the freedom in this way of living?

When we truly believe that God's grace is upon us, our spirit of striving subsides. Choosing God as the source of our love and resting in his grace empowers us to choose that which is constructive and beneficial in our lives. Slowly we find ourselves enjoying the gift of exercise or choosing to stop eating when we are comfortably satisfied. We begin to *want* to do that which is best, rather than that which feels like we *have* to.

Judy says, "Grace is freedom that conforms us from within; legalism is bondage that constrains us from without." Legalism, such as rigid dieting, binds and restricts the free will we have to make our own choices. It's imposed external pressure rather than an internal desire to live by the power of the Spirit within, as we choose to follow God's will.

• In what areas do you need to accept God's grace?

Legalism robs us of the ability to *want* to do something because we live under the pressure of *having* to. When we are under the law, we are compelled to do what the law says. When we live under grace, we are set free from the law and are led by the Holy Spirit (Galatians 5:18) who lives in us as followers of Christ. We're equipped to make choices that reflect the fruit of the Spirit: "love, joy, peace, patience, kindness, goodness, faithfulness, gentleness and self-control" (Galatians 5:22).

Take a moment to think about specific actions the fruit of the Spirit can equip you to make on your *HEAL* Journey. Specifically consider actions that relate to your daily encounters with food, your body, and your relationship with God and others. Feel free to refer to some of our examples.

Example:

Love: Basking in God's unconditional love allows me to accept the fullness of God's love for me and to extend it to others.

Gentleness: I can be gentle with myself in the way I treat and talk about my body.

Fruit of the Spirit Alive in My *HEAL* Journey

Love

_____

_____

_____

Joy

_____

_____

_____

Peace

_____

_____

_____

my reflections

_____

_____

_____

_____

_____

_____

_____

_____

_____

_____

_____

_____

_____

_____

_____

_____

_____

_____

my reflections

Patience

Kindness

Goodness

Faithfulness

Gentleness

Self-control

I like this section from the book *Thin Again*:

"In the case of those who struggle with disordered eating, the standard of legalism might be to be 'thin,' to achieve a certain weight at all costs, or the belief that when we 'lose' weight, life will be perfect and we will be free from all our problems. When we adopt external methods to constrain our behavior, we are buying the lie that victory can be won with our self-will. While 'losing weight' might result in an immediate increase in our sense of self-worth and value, it is temporary and does not change the deep-rooted feeling that we are irredeemably flawed nor does it satisfy our silent hunger for intimacy with God."

Janelle shares how she was set free from legalistic living:

"I used to be really legalistic in the way I ate and exercised. I was consumed by thoughts of what I should or should not eat and how much I should exercise. Legalism, compulsive eating, and exercising as well as my obsession with thinness became idols in my life. I was eventually filled with conviction for this sin and repented from my ways over time, and I invited God to take the reins of my life.

"I admit that it was really scary to accept God's grace and actively apply it to my eating because I was so worried that I would spin out of control. But with faith in God's strength, not my own, I took that scary first step of faith and was gently placed on the path of his grace and loving provision. It has taken some time, but over the past couple years, God has completely renewed my thinking.

"I no longer live, eat, and breathe legalism, but live a life that is in step with the Spirit. Rather than worrying about calories, carbohydrates, or fat grams, I ask myself if it's something God is leading me to enjoy and if it's what my body needs at that moment. I'm now living with freedom that equips me to make wise food choices. I have seen the fruit of the Spirit become ripe in my life as I enjoy the beauty of my time with God. My heart is now wide open to love people, to be joyful, to be good, to be gentle with myself and others, and to have self-control in light of God's grace."

my reflections

Janelle's Story

my reflections

- Reflect on how you can actively apply God's grace to your life and live a life led by the Spirit rather than by legalism.

Merciful Father,

Help me to live a life in step with your Holy Spirit—to bear good fruit that will honor you and bring you glory. Equip me through your Spirit to rise above the sinful nature of my desires, and grant me strength and wisdom to obey and trust the way you made my body. I thank you that, as your child, I can be set free to live an abundant life under the gift of your grace.

Accountability Moment

Remember, now's the time to call a girlfriend and share with her how things are going—and hear how she's doing, too.

No Forbidden Foods

As we have mentioned before, there are no forbidden foods on the *HEAL* Journey. We believe it's important that you be empowered to choose which foods you eat or drink as you reflect on God's grace. Of course, this isn't saying that all foods are equally beneficial to your body. That's definitely not the case! But having the freedom to enjoy *all* foods is especially healing after living in the prison of legalistic food rules, strict exercise regimens, or all or nothing thinking patterns.

God loves you the same whether you eat organic vegetables with tofu or a greasy burger and fries. Remember that such regulations "have an appearance of wisdom, with their self-imposed worship, their false humility and their harsh treatment of the body, but they lack any value in restraining sensual indulgence" (Colossians 2:23). Those rules aren't going to take away your desire for "forbidden" foods and probably won't keep you from eating them. They merely increase your focus on food and decrease your focus on God.

Know that God's perfect love can cast out your fears and allow you to embark on a freedom-filled way of eating and living. I pray that he will give you the courage to approach all foods with freedom and confidence! He wants to heal you and set you free!

_____

_____

_____

_____

_____

_____

_____

Letting Something Go

There may be a season on your *HEAL* Journey when you choose to eliminate certain foods or beverages because they are distancing you from God. While *HEAL* is a freedom-filled approach to food, in which you can eat any foods you want within the boundaries of hunger and fullness, it is sometimes helpful to refrain from a certain food or activity for a season if you feel it's detrimental to your healing journey.

One of my friends on the *HEAL* Journey, shares her experience:

"There was a time when I had to take a complete break from working out. I knew it would not remain that way forever, but I had become so obsessed about exercising that it totally took over my life. I felt like a failure if I didn't run eight miles a day. Exercise had become an idol in my life. I knew it was best for me to take a break during that season of life because God had to renew my mind and heal the way I thought about exercise. Since then, I've developed a healthier, balanced relationship with exercise. Now it's my opportunity to worship God and thank him for my wonderfully made body as I go for a walk or a bike ride."

Janelle shares a similar experience:

Janelle's Story

"I used to weigh myself sometimes as often as 10 times a day. God helped me realize that losing weight had become an unhealthy obsession and I needed to toss out the bathroom scale!"

Stumbling blocks for many girls include frequent weigh-ins, intense exercise regimens, energy drinks, alcohol, diet soda, coffee, sweets, and baked goods. I personally have made the decision to completely refrain from drinking alcohol because God revealed to me that it had the potential to be a problem in my life. The night of my high school graduation party, I was completely suffocated from the onset of a dark, debilitating depression. I was an emotional mess. Desperate to feel better, I went upstairs and grabbed a wine cooler from under my bed, which was left over from another party with my friends. Alone in my room, I shut the door and drank the entire bottle in two minutes, hoping it would loosen me up and make me feel better. A few years later, God showed me that alcohol had the potential to be a problem in my life because of my past struggle with depression. Knowing this and seeing firsthand how the overconsumption of alcohol ruined marriages, led to abuse, and caused much pain in my mom's family, I cut it completely out of my life, and I've never regretted my decision!

God may make it clear to you that he wants you to cut something out of your life that may not be serving you well. We can be confident that God has already declared victory in our lives because his Spirit now lives within us. This knowledge empowers us to rise above any temptation. In fact, God's Word assures us: "No temptation has seized you except what is common to man. And God is faithful; he will not let you be tempted beyond what you can bear. But when you are tempted, he will also provide a way out so that you can stand up under it" (1 Corinthians 10:13).

As much as I like this verse, a part of me would rather not hear it because it means that for all the times I've given in to temptation, God had provided a way out that I chose not to take. I hope this truth that God is faithful and that he will provide a way out when we are tempted is a refreshing truth for you, not a condemning one. Romans 8:37 assures us of this: "In all these things we are more than conquerors through him who loved us." Girls, how tremendously encouraging it is to know that we can live fearlessly in the light of this truth: There is no temptation you cannot rise above with God on your side.

my reflections

Free Space

Lesson 5: Group Study

An Aisle of Grace

Opening

Read Psalm 139 together.

Recap

Discuss this past week's lesson. What resonated with you? What did God teach you? Is there anything that stood out? Take time to discuss what you learned.

Sharing and Discussion

Reflect on the following thought from *Thin Again*:

"Striving for perfection, we are living the lie that we can make ourselves more acceptable to ourselves, to others, and to God if we just follow the letter of the law. Under grace we are free to turn to God as we really are, free to learn from our mistakes, free to change and grow, and free to allow him to help us become all he intends us to be."

Discussion Questions

• How does God want to lavish his grace upon you?

- How have you lived under legalism rather than grace?

- Reflect on the verse as a group:

  "Everything is permissible for me"—but not everything is beneficial. "Everything is permissible for me"—but I will not be mastered by anything (1 Corinthians 6:12).

- What does this verse mean to you?

Walking on the Tightrope of Perfection

Time for a fun activity!

Replicate a tightrope on the ground using a rope, chalk (if you're outside), or masking tape. Extend this for about 6 or 7 yards.

Blindfold one volunteer and help her place her feet on the beginning of the "tightrope." Back away and tell her to start walking on the tightrope. As she tries to balance upon this tightrope, call out legalistic commands such as "you have to exercise every day this week for two hours" or "you can't have that to eat." Once she has finished trying to walk upon this tightrope of perfection, take off her blindfold, kick the rope aside, take her hand, and gently guide her down a wide aisle that represents God's grace. As she walks upon this "aisle of grace," gently speak encouraging words reflective of God's grace and truth. Repeat this with all the girls, walking them down the aisle of grace and speaking words of truth and beauty to each one.

Once you're done, spend time as a group reflecting on this illustration, and discuss how you can apply what you've learned to your life.

Journaling

Make a list of all your favorite foods, whether or not they are a regular part of your diet. Then respond to the following questions:

- Do you allow yourself to eat all of these foods? Why or why not?

- Which foods do you ever restrict yourself from having?

- Are any of these foods ever stumbling blocks for you?

Verses on Grace

If time permits, look up the following verses on grace, and discuss them together:

—2 Corinthians 12:9

—Hebrews 4:16

—2 Corinthians 9:8

—Ephesians 2:5

Group Prayer

Break into pairs (or threes if needed) and take turns praying that one another will be able to grasp the reality of grace and apply it to our HEAL Journey.

Lesson 6: Abundant Living

Personal Study

Abundant living—I think Rick Warren, author of the bestselling book *The Purpose Driven Life,* sums it up perfectly: "It's not about you."

The story of our lives is woven into an eternal story written by the God of the universe. It's a story much bigger than any one of us. Just as you'll never discover your life's purpose apart from God, you'll never experience an abundant life apart from him, either. Jesus told us that he has come that we may have life and have it more abundantly (John 10:10). He is our hope for healing and the One who sets us free. A fabulous life results from pursuing God's glory, not our own.

- Take some time to reflect on how the world defines an abundant life. In the space to the right, capture your reflection in words, in a sketch, or in a song or poem. Feel free to get creative!

On your journey toward an abundant life, pray that God will equip you with the strength and courage to step out from the words of the world and into the words of the Father. We want to inspire you to stop looking inward and start looking upward to the Maker of all things. "Delight yourself in the Lord and he will give you the desires of your heart" (Psalm 37:4). God knows the desires of your heart—that you long for a life of adventure, freedom, romance, friendship, joy, and passion. As we lose ourselves in Christ and take delight in his love, his living water overtakes our souls. We slowly lose our thirst for things the world claims to offer, and we begin to thirst for a deeper relationship with him.

Made for So Much More

Somewhere in our pursuit of what the world offers, we come undone. In between working out at the gym, reading self-help books and People magazine, wasting time

my reflections

_____

_____

_____

_____

_____

_____

_____

on Facebook, pouring our hearts into unhealthy relationships, and trying to please everyone around us, we lose sight of the women God created us to be. We focus upon ourselves while the world before us hungers and cries out for our authentic beauty.

Each of us has a deeper calling:

"The Spirit of the Sovereign Lord is on me, because the Lord has anointed me to preach good news to the poor. He has sent me to bind up the brokenhearted, to proclaim freedom for the captives and release from darkness for the prisoners…to comfort all who mourn…to bestow on them a crown of beauty instead of ashes, the oil of gladness instead of mourning, and a garment of praise instead of a spirit of despair" (Isaiah 61:1-3).

Kayla, a college student on the *HEAL* Journey, reflects on her experience of living out this calling:

Kayla's Story

"I have found that by serving others, my view of my body completely altered. When working at a preschool for blind and disabled children, I never thought about my body and how I wanted to change it; instead, I rejoice in it! As we are reminded in HEAL, I have eyes to see, hands to serve, legs to run, and lips to kiss. I am body beautiful. When I am surrounded by these precious kids, I am impressed by the unique beauty God created in each of them. They are absolutely gorgeous with shining eyes, warm hugs, cute little feet, and smiles to light up the world! Whether it's Jacquie, who uses a talker instead of her voice, showing love through tight hugs, or Anthony, who walks with a guide dog twice his size but has a giggle that makes you want to dance, they all remind me constantly of the higher calling I have in Christ."

_____

_____

_____

The abundant life God calls us to is a life of service and self-sacrifice. Jesus didn't come into this world to be served, but to serve. He calls us to that as well. God reminds us that to whom much is given much is required (Luke 12:48). Our enemy would rather you chase beauty that will fade than fix your eyes upon the abundant, everlasting life you have in Christ. I like the way *The Message* states Romans 8:6,

"Obsession with self in these matters is a dead end; attention to God leads us out into the open, into a spacious, free life."

During a *HEAL* event one night, Haylie shared something that has stuck with me ever since:

"I think that if I had a penny for every time I thought negatively about my body, I could feed a hungry child for the rest of his life."

- List 10 ways your life might be different if you weren't preoccupied with food, eating, your weight, or how your body looks. What would you think about instead? How might you spend your time differently?

1. _____
2. _____
3. _____
4. _____
5. _____
6. _____
7. _____
8. _____
9. _____
10. _____

God-Breathed Friendship

Someone once said that friends are like a good bra: "Hard to find, supportive, comfortable, always lifts you up, never lets you down or leaves you hanging, and always near to your heart." I don't know if this analogy would have worked so well for me in high school since I didn't have much to be "lifted up," but I do know good friends are to be treasured and honored. However, even harder to find and more precious is a

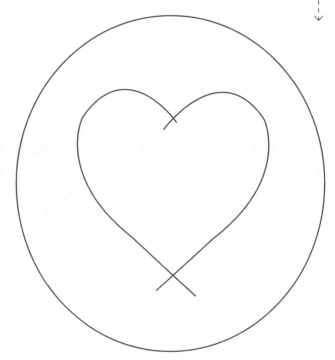

God-breathed friend—one who breathes the truth of God into your life through her words and actions. A God-breathed friend is always there to remind you of your true value and worth. She is a prayer warrior—ready and willing to speak to God on your behalf. She knows the voice of truth and is aware of the lies you are prone to believe. She sees the beauty that God has created in you even when you don't see it yourself.

The God-breathed friendships in my life—those built on a shared love and reverence for Christ—have produced unchanging bonds that endured and outshone friendships built only on similar interests, a common history, fun experiences, or mutual friends. Every time God brought such a friendship into my life, it was like I had known these girls forever. There was an unbreakable bond.

Stories of God-breathed friendship are found throughout the Bible. The story of Ruth and her widowed mother-in-law Naomi and the unmatched friendship between David and Jonathan are two good examples of God-breathed friendships. And when Jesus sent out his disciples, he commanded them to go in twos. Girls, we are not meant to do this life alone!

Take time to explore your friendships and relationships.

- Inside the heart, write the names of people who speak truth and love to you and who encourage you on your walk with God. Inside the circle surrounding the heart, list the names of people you care about but who may not necessarily uplift or encourage you... those who may not necessarily always be a positive influence in your life. Outside the circle list the names of anyone from whom you should distance or separate yourself... people who discourage you in life or on your *HEAL* Journey.

- Are there any relationships or friendships in your life that discourage you on your *HEAL* Journey by making you feel poorly about your body or intensifying your focus on food? What should be done about these relationships?

Let's look at how God-breathed friendships can encourage us specifically on the *HEAL* Journey:

—Commit to keep each other accountable for the way we talk about our bodies.

—Recognize that when you talk poorly about your body, others may begin to see themselves and you through your distorted lens.

—Live out the principles of *HEAL* together!

—Offer to pray regularly for, or with, one another.

—Remember that living in the light involves being honest about your sin with trusted, supportive friends and encouraging them to do the same.

My hope and prayer is that on the *HEAL* Journey you will be surrounded by God-breathed friends who will empower and encourage you with truth. If such friends are missing from your life, pray to God who gives generously, and he will be faithful.

Lindsey has seen God answer her prayers for Christ-centered friendships:

"About nine months ago I moved into an old, yellow Victorian house. I had been praying for two years that God would allow me to live in a Christian community. Little did I know how much God would go above and beyond this desire. The yellow house, or "yellow castle," as we sometimes call it, consists of five amazing women of God! I knew one of the girls when I moved in, but now each one of my roommates is like a kindred spirit. God has used each girl to speak truth into my life, to encourage me, to walk with me through trials, to laugh with me, cry with me, pray with me, and dance with me. They read and examine Scripture with me, dream, hope, and, above all, smile with me at the future (like the Proverbs 31 woman!) as we hold fast to God's promises. God has used each girl to minister to my spirit. And because I live in the midst of such amazing women of God, I have courage to continue on the path of righteousness. In fact, God has not only taken away my body image issues, he has been redeeming and healing all that had been lost and damaged through my life struggles for the past several years!"

Lindsey's Story

my reflections

_____

_____

_____

_____

_____

_____

_____

Life Abundantly

An abundant life doesn't mean a pain-free life. Jesus never promised us that this side of heaven, but he has promised us multiple times through his Word that he will never leave us or forsake us (Hebrews 13:5). It's not hard to recognize someone whose life encapsulates the abundance God has promised.

Kenon, an amazing woman I have been blessed to know, lives the abundant life in the midst of difficult circumstances. This mentor of mine shares the following testimony:

Kenon's Story

"As a teenager, I spent much of my time looking for abundance in ultimately unfulfilling ways: daily shopping trips searching for joy in a more flattering outfit, attention from guys to prove I was attractive, and attempting to perfect my body through extreme exercise and restrictive eating patterns. But God was pursuing me, and he would not allow me to be satisfied by these lesser pleasures.

"Before my senior year in high school, I went on a summer-long exchange program to Japan. As I was leaving to go overseas, a local Young Life leader gave me a Bible. Although I was from a non-Christian home, I was drawn to the Word as I was separated from all that was familiar. God did a miracle and revealed his beauty to me that summer, and I returned home having made the choice to follow Christ. Although my decision was unsupported at home, I experienced his peace and his direction to attend Westmont, a small Christian liberal arts college.

"As I studied his Word and got to know his people, my grip on the world's offers of 'the good life' was being loosened, and my security in him was strengthened. And as my faith deepened, he began to introduce powerful opportunities to know his loving presence. At age 21, I was diagnosed with

Hodgkin's disease—cancer of the lymphatic system—and added radiation to my daily schedule as a college senior. My cancer recurred the next year just as I was beginning to date a wonderful man. God again unveiled his love for me in allowing me to feel cherished in the midst of an extreme illness and the loss of all my hair. On our wedding day, I walked down the aisle wearing a wig, with my chemo catheter neatly pinned to my chest under the lace of my wedding dress. All the lies about body image that had imprisoned me for so long were completely disproved!

"Since then God has given me fullness of life in the face of daunting and 'abundant' road blocks. Just three years into our marriage, a bone marrow transplant (with a 50-50 chance of survival) was necessary. My only sister was a perfect match, even though we were opposite in every way. That same year, cancer-related menopause was diagnosed instead of a much longed-for pregnancy. For a couple who looked forward to having a big family, this was devastating news. But God once again proved himself able to accomplish the impossible. Over the course of seven years, three different birth moms chose Matt and me to adopt their babies. Our children, now 12, 8, and 4, are daily reminders of God's abundance and grace in our lives.

"Last year I faced cancer once again. With the diagnosis of breast cancer came a mastectomy, chemotherapy, and baldness. This time my children were able to see God's faithfulness at work. As his grace and mercy sustained me, he again entrusted me with the removal of exterior beauty. Each day overflows with gratefulness in the face of significant losses and challenges. He has shown me, time and again, that our abundant life is deeply rooted in his presence. No matter the circumstances, his love is confirmed and his beauty shines through me as mine is set aside—what a privilege."

Kenon's Story

_____

_____

_____

_____

_____

_____

_____

_____

_____

_____

_____

_____

_____

_____

_____

_____

_____

_____

_____

_____

_____

Action: Be Still Before God

Yup, you read it right. Be still before God. Earlier we talked about the sanctity of stillness before God. Before you read on, spend some time in total solitude before God. Feel free to reflect on your experience in this space.

Cultivating Inner Beauty

"Charm is deceptive, and beauty is fleeting; but a woman who fears the Lord is to be praised" (Proverbs 31:30).

"Your beauty should not come from outward adornment, such as braided hair and the wearing of gold jewelry and fine clothes. Instead, it should be that of your inner self, the unfading beauty of a gentle and quiet spirit, which is of great worth in God's sight. For this is the way the holy women of the past who put their hope in God used to make themselves beautiful" (1 Peter 3:3-5).

In these verses, God teaches us so much about the righteous beauty of a woman.

When I first heard them, however, I felt guilty for spending even a minute on my external appearance. But God isn't telling us not to beautify ourselves with makeup or jewelry or cute clothes; he's just telling us that our beauty will not come from such things. God wants us to cultivate inner beauty—the beauty within us that is unfading, never ceasing, and eternal! We're called to have a "gentle and quiet spirit." Let's explore what this character description really means.

Such a woman is at peace with her God. She trusts him completely as the number one relationship in her life. She understands where her true value and worth lies—that it's not in the clothes she wears, the guy she dates, or her socioeconomic background. She's fully aware of her identity as a beloved daughter of God. Her spirit is at rest— gentle and quiet because she knows that no matter what trouble comes her way, her future in Christ is secure. No amount of striving, accomplishments, or external beauty can make her more valuable or loved in the eyes of her Lord. That, my girl, is a beautiful woman!

Prayer Moment

Loving Father,

Give me the courage to step away from the words of the world and into your words. Jesus, I long for the abundant life you have promised us. Be with me as I surrender my heart, life, plans, and desires to you. I know full well that you will never leave or forsake me, but that your hand will guide me all of the days of my life. Thank you for your extravagant love.

my reflections

Free Space

Lesson 6: Group Study

Abundant Living

Opening

Read Psalm 139 together.

Recap

Discuss this past week's lesson. What resonated with you? What did God teach you? Is there anything that stood out in the writings? Take some time to discuss what you learned.

Read Romans 1:18-24 together as a group. Discuss how Paul's words reflect the condition of our society.

Have you been guilty of worshipping creation instead of the Creator?

Discuss the topic of God-breathed friendship. What did you discover in this section as you explored the relationships in your life?

Creative Activity

Gather a large pile of magazines, two larges pieces of poster board, glue, scissors, and markers.

Form two groups. The first group will cut out words and phrases (not pictures or images) that represent the life that the world offers and glue these to one sheet of newsprint. The other group will go through the Bible and write down on their newsprint Scriptures that refer to the abundant life God promises. You may want to offer a Bible dictionary or concordance to this group to help them in their searching.

Have everyone close their eyes as two representatives (one from each group) read the words aloud. Allow your group some time to reflect on this experience.

- What is it like to listen to the words of the world? How does your soul feel?

- What is it like to hear the voice of the Father spoken over your life?

Spend some time together in prayer.

Continuing Your Journey

Just because we've come to the end of our time together, it doesn't mean that this has to be the end of your *HEAL* Journey! We definitely encourage you girls to continue meeting regularly. Take time right now to talk about how this might look. Find out who would like to continue meeting, how often you'll get together, and what your time together as a group will look like. Be sure to visit our website at **www.healjourney.com** for encouragement, resources, and ideas!

Celebrate!

Now that you've finished this study, you deserve a celebration! Plan a fun event as a group so you can continue the God-breathed friendships you've established and celebrate the work God's done in your life these past weeks.

Also, please know that we'd love to hear from you! Share your stories of encouragement or transformation by e-mailing us at **HealJourney@gmail.com**.

Leader's Tips

- Be rooted in prayer.
- Hold an introductory and welcome meeting for all participants prior to having them begin Lesson 1. Go over the introduction together, and solidify your group's calendar.
- Assess the needs, time schedule, and desires of your group to determine whether you would like to spread the study out over six or 12 weeks.
- Prepare for each meeting with prayer, thoughtful consideration, and reflection.
- Be sure to reiterate the importance of confidentiality to the group members so that each girl feels comfortable, respected, and safe.
- Remember your role. In addition to being a part of the *HEAL* Journey, your role is to facilitate the group discussion in a way that fosters equal group participation, community, and encouragement.
- Be a conscious listener and do not monopolize the group discussion, but rather facilitate it.
- Do your best to keep the meetings encouraging and positive.
- Pray for the girls in *HEAL*, and think of ways to encourage them throughout the week.
- Plan fun events outside of your regular meeting times to help cultivate a sense of community and friendship.
- Consider offering regular support for the *HEAL* Journey once your group has finished this study.
- If you are concerned about the overall health and well-being of any of the participants, encourage them to seek professional help for a full evaluation and an in-depth course of treatment from a physician and licensed therapist.
- For more ideas and resources, please visit www.healjourney.com.

Hey Girls!

Thanks for being a part of the HEAL Journey! I pray that God will continue to shine his face upon you as you walk toward freedom in this area of your life. Be sure to visit the HEAL website at www.healjourney.com for more resources and encouragement including:

- Podcasts
- The HEAL Blog
- Online Store
- Booking Information for Retreats & Workshops

Keep in touch & God bless.

Love & Hugs,

Allie

HEAL | healthy eating & abundant living

www.healjourney.com